...sery Rhyme No. ... ...gular
speaker in schools and churches, ... with hundreds
of children each year.

Jo Dobbs has taught Key Stage 2 for ten years and is currently working with Years 1 and 2 (KS1) at Michael Syddall C of E (Aided) Primary School in North Yorkshire. She is RE Coordinator for her school and is also on the Board of Governors. Prior to the birth of her son two years ago, she was involved with the Resource Centre for the Diocese of Ripon and Leeds and on the Ripon and Leeds Diocesan Board of Education. Jo has recently gained an MA in Theology and Religious Studies (with a specialist pathway in Religious Education), and is training to be a Section 23 Inspector. She is co-author with Brian of *News and Tell!* and *Year-Round Assemblies*, both published under BRF's *Barnabas* imprint.

Important information

Photocopying permission

The right to photocopy material in *Beyond the Candle Flame* is granted for the pages that contain the photocopying clause: 'Reproduced with permission from *Beyond the Candle Flame* published by BRF 2006 (ISBN 1 84101 431 1)', so long as reproduction is for use in a teaching situation by the original purchaser. The right to photocopy material is not granted for anyone other than the original purchaser without written permission from BRF.

The Copyright Licensing Agency (CLA)

If you are resident in the UK and you have a photocopying licence with the Copyright Licensing Agency (CLA), please check the terms of your licence. If your photocopying request falls within the terms of your licence, you may proceed without seeking further permission. If your request exceeds the terms of your CLA licence, please contact the CLA directly with your request. Copyright Licensing Agency, 90 Tottenham Court Rd, London W1T 4LP. Tel 020 7631 5555; fax 020 7631 5500; email cla@cla.co.uk; web www.cla.co.uk. The CLA will provide photocopying authorization and royalty fee information on behalf of BRF.

BRF is a Registered Charity (No. 233280)

Beyond the Candle Flame

Thirty reflective Bible stories for
quiet moments with 5-7s

Brian Ogden & Jo Dobbs

Text copyright © Brian Ogden and Jo Dobbs 2006
Illustrations copyright © Simon Smith 2006

The authors assert the moral right
to be identified as the authors of this work

Published by
The Bible Reading Fellowship
First Floor, Elsfield Hall
15–17 Elsfield Way, Oxford OX2 8FG
Website: www.brf.org.uk

ISBN 1 84101 431 1
ISBN-13 978 1 84101 431 9

First published 2006
10 9 8 7 6 5 4 3 2 1 0
All rights reserved

Acknowledgments
Scripture quotations are taken from the Contemporary English Version of
the Bible published by HarperCollins Publishers, copyright © 1991,
1992, 1995 American Bible Society.

A catalogue record for this book is available from the British Library

Printed in Singapore by Craft Print International Ltd

Contents

Part Two: Seasons

Part Three: Feelings

Foreword

Knowing that schools are required to provide opportunities for pupils' spiritual development across the whole curriculum is one thing; providing teachers with practical support to enable them do so is another. In putting this book together, the authors have successfully matched curriculum requirements to the reality of the busy primary classroom.

All children have the capacity to reach beyond the ordinary and the mundane, to wonder at the beauty and mystery of the world and to explore questions of meaning. However, the authors know from personal experience that for some children this process can be difficult, as they do not have the necessary skills. Their response is a lively book that offers teachers starting points to enable young children to develop skills that will enhance their spiritual growth.

Teachers will welcome the fact that the book adopts a simple strategy for structuring pupils' learning. Bible stories are linked to pupils' own experience and introduced in ways that enable children to use their imagination to explore their feelings and offer a considered response to the story. Through the development of listening and questioning skills and an increasing ability to sit still through the provision of 'quiet moments', these enjoyable learning experiences will contribute to pupils' spiritual development.

Busy teachers who do not wish to reinvent the wheel will welcome the supportive and accessible ideas in the book and should feel confident about using them flexibly, adapting them to their own contexts and the individual needs of their pupils.

If you are interested in the development of the whole child through activities that stimulate reflection and deepen pupils' responses, you will find the book an invaluable resource—thanks, Brian and Jo.

Eileen Bellett, RE Adviser for the Diocese of Ripon and Leeds

Introduction

The aim of this book is to begin to develop spirituality in young children as they learn about different stories from the Bible. The units also aim to form a foundation for Circle Time, where listening to each other and expression of the children's own feelings can be fostered and developed.

Preparing the session

Each unit has a theme and is based on a Bible verse or verses. Each session includes suggestions of artefacts (objects) that the children can hold or focus on. You may wish to arrange the artefacts into a tableau by placing them on a base cloth and including a candle in the grouping. The tableau can then be placed in the centre of the circle, so that the children can use it as a focal point.

Safety first

When using candles, always place them in holders, well out of reach of the children. Have ready a candle snuffer to extinguish the candles, a bucket of water for emergencies, and a bucket of damp sand in which to place the candles after use. Never leave lighted candles unattended.

Introducing the session

There may be some related discussion in the introduction to the main story. This is intended to enable the children to understand better what is happening in the story and to imagine what is taking place. At the back of the book is a list of suggested pieces of music that may accompany each story. The music should be very much in the background, and is used to set the mood for each session so that the children are immediately alerted to the fact that it is something 'special' and different from other activities.

Bible passages

Each story is based on a Bible passage that illustrates the theme of the session. A full list of the Bible passages used can be found at the back of the book to assist the cross reference between RE and PSHE/Circle Time.

Using the story

After the introduction, the main story can be read. During this part of the activity, the children are intended to be listening and imagining what is happening. It is hoped that through this section the children will learn about different Bible stories. The leader may need to explain to the children that there are often questions to think about, but that they don't need to be answered until the end; the questions are there to help them to think about what is happening.

Using the quiet moment

Following the story, there is a quiet moment. It is important that this time is maintained to enable the children to think about the story, consider their reaction to it and begin to formulate any questions that they may have.

Follow-up

During the follow-up, the children may raise their questions and explore what has happened in the story. The leader may need to prompt with questions of their own. This part of the activity will require careful management, so that the children learn not to talk over others or interrupt them. It might be appropriate to have an object that can be passed around the circle, the child holding the object being the one whose turn it is to speak. If this method is used, it is important that the children should not feel under any pressure to speak if they don't want to.

Final prayer

The prayer can be used to round off the whole activity if desired.

Preparing the children for a quiet space

The following instructions can be used before the story, to remind the children what is expected of them. If they are repeated on a regular basis, the children will quickly learn how to sit, listen and react to what they have heard in an appropriate manner, thus forming the foundation for effective Circle Time.

- Sit in a circle.
- Sit so that you are not touching the person next to you, with your legs crossed and your hands in your lap.
- Relax your body and let your shoulders drop a little. Make sure you feel comfortable.
- Close your eyes and think about your breathing. Make it steady, and think about breathing in and out slowly.
- Listen to the sounds in the room for a few moments. Can you hear noises from outside?
- Now, I want you to listen carefully to what I'm going to say. I'm going to tell you about something, and while I'm talking I'll ask you to think about different things.
- Try to make a picture in your head about the story, and at the end we'll have a chat about what you thought of.
- Try to sit still while you listen, as it will help you to think.
- Keep your eyes closed (or focused on the object) until I tell you to open them at the end.

Part One

SENSES

Senses 1

Jesus heals blind Bartimaeus

 Theme
The gift of sight

 Bible verse
Mark 10:46–52

 Artefact
A small bowl or piece of cloth with a few coins in it

Introduction

What do we say of people who cannot see? What do you think causes people not to be able to see? Just imagine putting on your clothes in the morning. What would be difficult about that if you couldn't see?

What is a beggar? Why would a person who couldn't see have to beg for money?

Show the children a picture of Jerusalem in Jesus' time. Talk about how the houses are different from modern houses in this country.

Not just another day

Slowly… close your eyes. What can you see? Nothing. When our eyes are closed we are unable to see at all. Imagine what it must be like to live like that. Not seeing where you are. Not seeing the food in front of you. Not seeing if it is safe to cross the road. Not seeing the person sitting next to you. How would you manage?

Using our imagination, we're going back to Bible times. Your home is in the town of Jericho. It's about 15 miles from Jerusalem. Every morning you leave your house. You walk slowly to the gate of the town. You walk slowly because you cannot see where you are going. You are blind. Do you think people help you? Can you recognize some of the voices?

'Hello, Bartimaeus,' says one familiar voice.

'How are you today?' says another.

'Watch out, Bartimaeus!' shouts a third. 'There's a deep hole just in front of you.'

So it's another day begging by the gate of the town. Can you feel the sun beating down? Every now and then, the dust blows in your face as a donkey is ridden past you. What a way to spend every day—calling out as you hear footsteps coming, your hand held in front of you, hoping for a coin. Will people be kind and give you money?

There seem to be a lot of people about today. Then you remember… in a day or two is the feast of Passover. Hundreds of people will be coming through the town on their way to Jerusalem. Can you hear the name everyone is talking about? Yes, that's right, it's Jesus. Yes, you've heard about Jesus. Didn't someone say that he heals people who are unwell?

Perhaps... just perhaps... Jesus could help you. Perhaps Jesus could make you see. That would be fantastic after all these years in the dark. Fancy seeing children's faces. Fancy seeing trees and animals and mountains. But will he help you? How will he even know you're there?

The crowd is pushing round you. Something must be happening. What are people saying? Jesus is coming. He's coming down the road. He will soon be passing through the gate just where you're sitting.

'Son of David! Jesus! Have pity on me!' You have never shouted louder.

'Be quiet, Bartimaeus,' some people in the crowd shout at you. But they don't know what it's like living in the dark.

'Jesus, help me!' You shout even louder. The crowd goes quiet. Jesus is speaking.

'Call him over,' says Jesus.

'Come on,' says a friendly voice in the crowd. 'He's calling for you.'

You jump up, throw off your dusty cloak, and run stumbling towards the voice.

'What do you want me to do for you?' asks Jesus.

'Master, I want to see!' you say.

Then he says the words you have waited your whole life to hear.

'Your eyes are healed because of your faith.'

Slowly, through a fog at first, you can see. You can see

Jesus standing in front of you. The crowd is around him. For the first time you see the town where you live. How do you feel? What do you say? What do you think about the people you are looking at? Are they as you imagined them? What do you notice about their clothes? Are the colours bright? Do they surprise you?

Follow-up

Draw a picture of Jesus and Bartimaeus with the crowd. How will Bartimaeus' face look? Will he be happy? Will he be surprised? How will the rest of the crowd look? What kind of clothes will people be wearing?

Prayer

Dear Father God, thank you that we are lucky enough to be able to see the wonderful things that you have created in your world. Thank you that we can watch tiny creatures as they move along the ground, that we can look at huge trees moving in the wind and that we can see all the beautiful colours around us. Help us to learn to say 'thank you' for the gift of sight and to use our eyes to watch everything around us. Amen

Senses 2

The girl who was made well

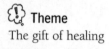 **Theme**
The gift of healing

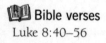 **Bible verses**
Luke 8:40–56

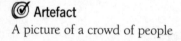 **Artefact**
A picture of a crowd of people

Introduction

Ask the children if they've ever been in a really crowded place. How did it feel? Have they ever seen someone on TV who was talking to a large group of people?

Have they ever known someone who was poorly and then got better? Were they worried when the person was poorly?

The poorly daughter

Slowly… close your eyes. You're back in Bible times. You are sitting in a tree-top and you can see a big group of people all jostling and pushing. They are trying to hear a man speak. It's Jesus! You remember seeing him when he made Bartimaeus better. There's another man talking to Jesus. You hear someone call out to him—his name is Jairus. Through the noise you can just hear Jairus pleading with Jesus.

'Please, Master, come quickly. My daughter is ill. We think she is dying,' he says. 'She's my only child, she's all that I have. Come and make her well again.'

'I will come and see her,' Jesus says, 'and I will try to help her if I can. Show me the way.'

As Jesus changes direction to walk with Jairus, the crowd all move round to follow him. They're still pushing and shoving, as they all want to be close to him.

'Let me in!' shouts one woman.

'No, let me be first!' shouts another.

You can see that they all want to be next to Jesus and hear what he is saying. Just as Jesus is moving away from you, you notice that he stops where he is. You can see that something is wrong. You listen really hard.

'Who touched me?' he asks.

What a strange thing to say, you think to yourself. Lots of people want to touch him and they are all pushing to be near him.

Peter speaks up and says, 'Master, the people are crowding and pressing against you.'

But again, Jesus says, 'Someone touched me, I know. The power has gone out of me.'

Then a woman steps forward out of the crowd. She is wearing long dark robes and she is bent over. She is crying and you can see that she is really nervous.

'I touched you, Lord,' she says. 'I have been bleeding for many years and no one can make me better, so I touched you because I knew I would be healed, and I have been. Forgive me.'

Then Jesus does a strange thing. He bends down to the woman and says, 'Daughter, your faith has healed you. Go in peace.' And he takes her hand and lifts her up.

Then there's a mumbling noise in the crowd. A man pushes his way to get close to Jesus and Jairus. He speaks to Jairus.

'Your daughter is dead,' he says. 'Don't bother Jesus any more.'

Jesus hears the man, and he says to Jairus, 'Don't be afraid, and she will be healed.'

Jesus starts to move off again, and once more the crowd jostle and push around him. He is leading them to Jairus' house. You climb down from your tree. You know a short cut to Jairus' house, so you run round to get ahead of the crowd. By the time they all get there, you have found a window to look through so that you can still see what is happening.

Jairus leads Jesus into the house. Only James, Peter and John go in with them. Some people in the crowd start to cry because they think the little girl has died, but Jesus tells them to stop. He says that the little girl is not dead, but asleep.

The people laugh at Jesus because they don't believe him. Jesus goes up to the little girl and takes her hand. He speaks to her gently and tells her to get up.

Then, slowly, she opens her eyes and sits up. She gets out of her bed and walks over to her mother and father, and they give her a huge hug.

Jesus tells her parents to give her something to eat, and they thank him with tears running down their cheeks.

Follow-up

Talk about the picture you have just imagined in your head. Which part of the story did you like best? Why? Did you think that Jesus would be able to make the little girl better? Can you imagine how her family would have felt after Jesus came to see her? Can you imagine how Jairus and his wife are feeling, and the woman in the crowd who was healed?

As we go round the group, if you want to you can tell us some of the things that you imagined in the picture in your head. You don't have to say anything if you don't want to.

Prayer

Dear Lord Jesus, you did some amazing things when you lived on earth. Thank you that you made people's lives better in lots of different ways. Help us to learn from your example and try to help people when they need it. Amen

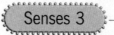

Senses 3

Enough food for all

 Theme
The gift of nourishment

 Bible verses
Luke 9:10–17

 Artefacts
A basket containing five small loaves and two fish shapes cut from shiny paper
A picture of a remote place in the countryside of Israel

Introduction

Talk about your favourite foods. Talk about times when you've been really hungry. How does it feel to have something to eat when you are very hungry? What kind of things might you do that mean you would miss a meal time? (For example, playing out.)

He must be very special

Slowly… close your eyes. You are in a place called Bethsaida. There is not much here, just a few houses and a lot of open fields. There are a few trees but not many. The ground is very dry and dusty. The sun shines brightly in the sky and it is very hot.

Jesus has come here to be with his disciples. There are twelve men with Jesus, and they want to be alone together and quiet. That's why they chose this place, away from all of the crowds that have been following them. They want to spend time praying to God, and talking about things that they have done, and trying to learn from Jesus all about the kingdom of heaven.

But some people saw them, and they told their friends, and soon there was a large group of people near Jesus. You are with the group and you can see that they want to talk to Jesus and they want him to teach them about God and heaven.

'I need to know what to do with my money,' says one man.

'I want to know what happens when I die,' says another.

You can hear them all saying the things they want to ask Jesus. Gradually more and more people come, and Jesus welcomes them and invites them to come and sit with him.

'Come to me,' Jesus calls, and they walk towards him or they are carried by their friends. Jesus puts his hands on them and prays, and the people are made well again. One man comes back and sits down near to you.

'I can't believe it!' he exclaims. 'I have had pain in my back for years and I couldn't walk straight, but now I feel like I can skip and dance, and the pain has completely gone. Jesus is truly a remarkable man.'

Then Jesus starts to talk about God and what it will be like in heaven. As it gets late, you see Jesus' special friends come up to him.

'Master, time is getting on,' they say. 'Send the crowd away into the villages nearby so that they can get something to eat and drink, and somewhere to stay, because there is nothing here except fields.'

But Jesus replies, 'You give them something to eat.'

'But we only have five loaves of bread and two fish,' they answer. 'Unless we go out and buy food for the crowd.'

Jesus says to them, 'Make the people sit in groups of about fifty.'

So the disciples start putting people into groups of fifty, and you watch as they all shuffle into the places where they've been told to sit.

Then, everyone looks at Jesus. He holds the five loaves and two fish up to heaven and says, 'Thank you, Father, for this food.'

After that, he starts to break up the loaves and the fish and share it around the crowd. The disciples pass round the baskets with the fish and bread in them. As the basket is passed to your neighbour, you hear him say, 'There's loads of food in here, but how can that be? We only had a small amount to share.'

When everybody has had enough to eat, the disciples gather up what is left. There are twelve baskets full of food left over! Jesus has done another miracle. He has made the small amount of food feed over five thousand people, and there is still some left over.

'I can't believe this man,' you hear your neighbour say. 'He makes people well again, he teaches about God and he makes a small amount of food feed a huge crowd. He is an amazing man! He must be very special.'

Follow-up

Think about the picture in your mind. Can you imagine what the crowd looked like as they shared the food round?

What did the people look like who were healed by Jesus? Can you remember what your neighbour said about his illness? Did you notice that so much time had passed by while Jesus was teaching? Can you imagine being in such a huge crowd?

As we go round the group, if you want to you can tell us something about your picture that you imagined, but you don't have to if you don't want to.

Prayer

Dear Father God, thank you that you sent Jesus to teach us all about you. Thank you that we can still learn about all that he did when we read the Bible. Thank you also that we have enough food to eat, and that we don't really know what it is like to be truly hungry. Amen

Senses 4

The wedding at Cana

 Theme
The gift of taste

 **Bible verses**
John 2:1–11

Artefact
Wedding photographs

Introduction

Discuss the wedding photographs with the children. Has anyone been a bridesmaid or page boy? Has anyone been to a wedding? What happens at a wedding? Who are the main characters at a wedding?

Discuss all the preparations that might have to be made, including the reception afterwards. What would the children expect to eat? What might adults be drinking?

A wonderful wedding

Slowly… close your eyes. Yes, you've guessed, we are going to a wedding. Not a wedding today but a wedding when Jesus was on earth. The wedding is taking place in Cana, a small village in Galilee, quite near to Nazareth where Mary, Joseph and Jesus lived. We don't know for sure, but it seems likely that Mary knew the family very well.

Weddings in those days were very different from the marriages we have today. The wedding took place in the evening after a feast. So let's join the happy crowd at the wedding feast. It looks as though everyone who lives in the village is here. Can you smell the food? I wonder if you will like it? Try a bit.

Although it is nearly dark, we can just see a small group of men joining all the others. I think it is Jesus with a few of his friends. What do you think? Yes, I'm sure it is; Mary has just gone over to greet him.

Mary is looking worried. I wonder what the problem is. She is pointing towards the wine. It looks as though they might be running a bit short.

Oh dear, that would be terrible. If they run out of wine at their wedding, the young couple will never live it down. People will talk about them for ever. 'Do you see them? It was their wedding where the wine ran out!'

Mary is talking to the waiters. Did you hear what she said? 'Do whatever Jesus tells you to do.' Mary knows that

Jesus will help if he can.

But what's happening now? The waiters are filling up those six huge water jars… with water! Those jars must hold about 100 litres each. The water is normally used for washing people's hands and feet because everything is so dusty and dirty.

Listen, Jesus has spoken to the waiters now that the jars are full.

'Now take some water and give it to the man in charge of the feast.' We would call him the Master of Ceremonies. One of the waiters has dipped a cup into the water. He's taking it to that rather grand-looking man over there.

The Master of Ceremonies is sniffing the water. Now he's sipped some and now he is looking quite amazed. He has gone over to speak to the bridegroom. Quick, see if you can hear what he's saying.

'The best wine is always served first, but you have kept the best until last!' Something wonderful must have happened to the water. It has become wine. Jesus has saved the day. The new bride and bridegroom won't be disgraced after all. Everyone is looking much happier and there's quite a queue to taste the new wine!

When the feast is over, the wedding ceremony takes place. Let's wait and see what happens next. It's quite dark now and the men are holding lighted torches—no, not the sort with batteries! A canopy is being held over the head of the newlyweds and they are walking round the village. People who didn't come to the wedding are coming out and shouting good wishes.

At last, having walked right round the village streets, the

couple have come to the new husband's house. For the next week they will stay there dressed in their wedding clothes. Lots of friends and relations will be visiting them. What a happy way to celebrate a wedding.

You know, if you read the stories about Jesus, you'll see that he loved parties. I'm sorry we didn't get to taste any of the wine, but at least we did go to the party.

Follow-up

How do you think the people at the wedding would have felt? Did you imagine their happy faces? Could you hear all of the chatter? Did the food look good in the picture in your head?

As we go round the circle, if you want to you can share something that you imagined when the story was being told.

Prayer

Dear Lord Jesus, you had many friends when you lived on earth, but you never forgot how they would all be feeling. You were there to share the good times, just as you were there when times were hard. Thank you that you are still with us in our lives, and that you help us when we ask you. Amen

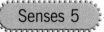

Senses 5

The Lord's supper

 Theme
The gift of companionship

 Bible verses
Matthew 26:26–30

 Artefacts
A goblet and a plate
Some bread and some blackcurrant juice

Introduction

Talk about times when we share meals together. It might be school lunch times, breakfasts or tea times at home.

When have the children shared special meal times? They might be parties, Sunday lunches with family, meals out at restaurants and so on. What have they enjoyed about these times?

A special meal

Slowly… close your eyes. You are in the town of Bethany. You can see Jesus. He is talking to his special friends. They seem to be talking excitedly. You lean in closer to listen to what they are saying.

'It will soon be time for the special festival of Passover,' says Peter.

'I like seeing lots of friends at this time,' Levi adds.

'No, the best part is the food we eat,' argues Andrew.

James disagrees. 'I like the stories that the older people tell. Sometimes they change parts from year to year.'

John is listening to all that the others are saying. He goes up to Jesus and says, 'Master, where do you want us to make the preparations for you to eat the Passover meal?'

Jesus answers, 'Go into the city and you will find a man. He will be carrying a water jug so you will know who he is. Tell him that we are going to celebrate the Passover at his house.'

Next you see the disciples chatting together, making lists of things to do.

'I'll go and get the food,' volunteers Andrew. 'That's the bit I like best.'

'I'll come and help you carry it,' says James.

'Well, I'll go and get some wine to drink,' suggests Peter.

'And we'll go and find the man in the city,' add Levi and John.

You are interested in this man who is going to look after

everybody, so you quietly follow Levi and John. They find the man they are looking for.

'Sir, the Master says that you are to let us use your house for the celebrations,' the disciples say.

'Ah, yes! I've been expecting you,' the man answers. 'How many of you will there be?'

'Well, there are twelve of us and the Master,' replies John.

'Right, I'll get on with making the room ready,' he says. Then he disappears off towards his house.

You decide to follow him. Luckily for you, there are some olive trees next to the house and you are really good at climbing them. You decide that you want to see what is going to happen. So you go back and get yourself a drink and something to eat from the town, and then you find the man's house again, and climb up into the trees nearby. You can clearly see into the upstairs window, so you settle yourself there and decide to wait.

You look up and you can see some men coming into the room. Yes, you recognize the man who owns the house. He's showing the others where they can sit.

They sit down to eat. First they pray and give thanks for the food, and then they start to share all the different types of things to eat. Then the men start to become more serious. You can see Jesus breaking a piece of bread and sharing it out to everybody. Then he starts to say something, so you lean in closer to hear what he's saying.

'Take this and eat it. This is my body.'

The others all eat a small piece of the bread, but they don't say anything. Then you hear Jesus talking again.

'Drink from this cup, all of you. This is my blood, which

is poured out to forgive you all of your sins.'

Then you see all of the men pass round the cup and drink from it. The men have gone quiet. It is as if they know something is going to happen that will make them feel sad.

Then Levi starts to hum a tune. They are all joining in and adding words to it. It goes on for quite a while. The song thanks God for many different things.

When the song is finished, you see them all gradually stand up and leave the room. As you watch, they thank the man who owns the house, and they go out into the street and start to walk towards the hill outside the town.

Follow-up

Talk about the picture you imagined in your head. Which part of the story did you like best? Why? What did the disciples look like? Did you like the feeling of being able to look into the room and hear what was going on? Did it make you feel part of the celebrations?

As we go round the group, if you want to you can tell us about the picture you imagined. You don't have to if you don't want to.

Prayer

Dear Lord Jesus, you showed us many different ways to remember you. You showed us how to get along with each other, and you showed us how to care for all of the things that God made. When we see people sharing food together, help us to remember how much you loved people when you were alive on earth and how much you love us now. Thank you for being our friend. Amen

Senses 6

Jesus heals a man who was deaf

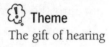 **Theme**
The gift of hearing

 **Bible verses**
Mark 7:31–37

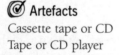 **Artefacts**
Cassette tape or CD
Tape or CD player

Introduction

For a minute or so, just ask the children to listen really hard without making a sound. What can they hear? Talk about when you need to be able to hear. (Play the tape or CD.)

Tell the children that in Jesus' time, most of the learning was done by telling people things. There was very little written down because very few people could write, so it was really important to be able to hear.

Jesus helps a deaf man

Slowly... close your eyes. You're back in Jesus' time and you are near the Sea of Galilee. It's a really busy place. There are a lot of fishermen with many boats, trying to catch enough fish to feed their own families and sell some extra to get some money.

There are also some women sitting near the shore, with huge fishing nets spread out on their knees and on the ground around them. It looks as if they are doing some sewing. You get quite interested in this, and as you walk closer you realize that they are mending the holes in the nets so that the fish can't escape. As they work, they chatter to each other. You hear that one of the women is called Ruth.

You look over to where an old man called Reuben is sitting. He's also mending nets, and every so often he stops to look out to sea. He must have a very strange life, as he can't even hear the quiet sound of the water lapping at the edge of the shore.

Your thoughts are broken by a noise in the distance. Reuben senses something and looks in the same direction as you, and even the women stop their conversation. You can just make out a crowd of people coming towards the lake, led by a tall man. As they get nearer, you can hear the people calling out.

'Tell us another story, Teacher.'

'Yes, I want to hear the one about the farmer sowing the grains of seed.'

'No, we heard that one the other day,' argues the first voice. 'Tell us another story. What about one to do with the lake?'

A short distance away, Jesus spots a piece of ground a little way away from where you are sitting. It is higher up than you are, so you can see everything really clearly.

'Do any of you here have troubles? Come and talk to me,' he says.

'What about Reuben?' asks Ruth's friend. 'Why don't we take him to the Master?'

'What harm could it do?' asks Ruth. 'Come on.'

Together, the women put down their nets and walk over to Reuben, who has been watching all of this going on. He seems a little confused when they approach him, but gently they bend down and help him to his feet. They walk him over to where Jesus is standing. The women bow their heads.

Ruth says, 'Please, Lord, help this gentle man. He cannot hear and he does not have the power of speech.'

Jesus puts his fingers into Reuben's ears. Then he spits and touches Reuben's tongue. Then he looks up to heaven and, with a deep sigh, says, 'Be opened.'

As he says this, Reuben suddenly looks shocked and he puts his hands to his ears. He looks quickly around the crowd and at the two women.

'Praise be to God!' he shouts. 'I can hear, I can speak!'

Then, just as quickly, he drops to his knees in front of Jesus and thanks him. Jesus says in a loud voice so that all of the crowd could hear him, 'None of you here must say anything of what you have just seen. You must not tell anyone.'

But it is no use, the crowd is buzzing with excitement. And Reuben seems to have a lifetime of talking to catch up on. He is walking from person to person in the crowd, asking them all kinds of things about what they do, and where they live. At each answer, you can see that he is overjoyed to be able to hear what they say.

Ruth turns to her friend and says, 'He has done everything well.'

'Yes, he even makes the deaf hear and the mute speak,' answers her friend.

Follow-up

Which parts of the story did you manage to picture in your head? Were there any parts that you particularly liked? Could you imagine what the women, or Reuben, looked like?

As we go round the circle, if you want to you can tell us about the picture you had in your head.

Prayer

Dear Father God, you give us so many gifts that sometimes it's hard to think what it must be like not to have them. Thank you that Jesus came to our world and taught us how to be more grateful for what we have. Help us to help people who are not as fortunate as we are. Amen

An angel tells about the birth of John

 Theme
The gift of speech

Bible verses
Luke 1:1–25 and 62–64

Artefact
An incense stick (or cone) to light so that the children can smell it and see the smoke swirl

Introduction

Talk about all the different ways we use our voices—chatting to friends, telling stories, reading aloud, shouting, singing, and so on. What might it be like to have no voice? Have you ever had a sore throat that made it difficult to speak? How would you tell people things if you couldn't speak to them? What might you use?

A special couple

Slowly… close your eyes. You have gone way, way back in time to just before Jesus was born. The land is very hot and dry. You can see in front of you an old man and an old woman. They look like kind people and seem to have a lot of friends, but there also seems to be a sadness in their eyes because they have no family of their own.

As you watch them, you see Zechariah kiss his wife and go towards the temple. You can still see him, and you decide to follow him into the temple. Once inside, he greets other priests and then he finds a place and kneels down to pray in a quiet voice, almost a whisper.

'Father God, every day since I came here, I have asked you that Elizabeth and I might have a son. Thank you, Lord, for listening to your humble servant. Amen.'

Then you watch as he slowly gets up, wipes the tears from his eyes and goes towards the high altar. There, you see him talking to the other priests as they decide who will take the next few services in the temple.

It is Zechariah's turn next. You see him lighting some incense and you watch in fascination as it swirls and twirls up towards the ceiling. You can hear a group of people gathering outside the temple, and you can hear them starting to pray.

As you look back to the altar where Zechariah is burning the incense, you see a movement. It's not very clear, so you peer into the smoke, and then you hear a deep voice.

'Do not be afraid, Zechariah. I am an angel of the Lord. Your prayer has been heard. Your wife Elizabeth will bear you a son, and you are to give him the name John. He will be a great joy and a delight to you, and many people will rejoice because of his birth. Many people will come back to God because of him.'

Zechariah, although frightened at first, finds his courage and answers, 'How can I be sure of this? I am an old man and my wife is also well on in years.'

The angel replies, 'I am Gabriel. I have been sent by God. Because you did not believe me, you will be silent and not able to speak until this happens.' Then the smoke clears a little and the angel is gone.

Meanwhile, the people are waiting outside the temple, wondering what has happened to Zechariah, as he's been gone a long time. When he comes out, he can't speak. One of them shouts out, 'He must have seen a vision.'

You watch as Zechariah nods to show that he has seen a vision. He can't say a word.

Time passes before you see Zechariah and Elizabeth again. They seem to be getting ready to go out. They are going back to the temple again with a baby. He is their son! They walk there and give the baby to the priest who is going to name him.

'What name do you give this child?' he asks.

'His name is to be John,' Elizabeth answers.

'But you don't have anyone in your family with that name,' says a friend of theirs.

Then Zechariah shows that he wants to write something down. They find him a writing tablet and a stick. He write, 'His name is John.'

And as soon as he does this, he is able to speak.

'I can speak again, I can speak! Praise God! Praise God for this beautiful baby! Thank you, Lord, for answering the prayers of your servant!'

The friends nearby are shocked and then they start to smile.

'This is truly amazing,' says one man.

'Let us go and tell all the village that Zechariah can speak again,' says a woman.

You watch as gradually the friends spread out, telling the good news. You look back and see Zechariah standing next to Elizabeth. She is holding the baby John and they are both looking at him and smiling. Then Zechariah kisses the top of his wife's head and she looks up to smile at him.

Follow-up

Did you enjoy the story? Which parts did you like best? Can you imagine how relieved Zechariah must have felt when he was able to speak again?

Could you picture what the angel might have looked like as he appeared through the incense smoke?

As we go round the circle, you can tell us about parts of your picture in your head, if you want to.

Prayer

Lord God, thank you for the gift of speech. It is wonderful to be able to talk to friends, and to sing, and to shout, and to join in with all kinds of different things. Help us to use our gift of speech wisely, and to say only good things and not things that will hurt others. Thank you, Lord. Amen

Senses 8

Firm foundations

 Theme
The gift of being the best that we can be

 Bible verses
Luke 6:46–49

 Artefacts
A house brick
A lump of rock
A pile of sand

Introduction

Talk about building towers with wooden blocks. What happens when you put the blocks on the table before you start to build? Do they stay where they are?

What happens if you build in the sandpit? What do the blocks do? Why do you think this is?

The two builders

Slowly… close your eyes. You are back in the time of Jesus, and as usual there is a crowd of people round him. The crowd are near the shore of a lake, and the sun is bright as it reflects off the water. They are all shouting out questions to him, but they are also listening really carefully to the answers.

'Lord, how can I forgive a man who has stolen from me?' asks one man.

'Forgive him, and God will forgive you all of your sins,' Jesus answers.

The crowd murmurs in agreement, and a few people turn to their friends to say things, but they speak in whispers so you can't quite hear.

'Teacher, how should I give to those less fortunate than me?' asks a woman.

'Give to everyone who asks you, and if anyone takes something that belongs to you, don't ask for it back,' Jesus replies.

'But Lord, there are always so many beggars,' the woman answers.

'Give generously, and it will be given back to you by God. The more you give to others in this life, the more your Father in heaven will give to you. If you give nothing, then your Father will give you nothing. If you give plenty, then in heaven you will have many blessings.'

Another man asks, 'Lord, how do I learn to stop arguing with my neighbour? He is always trying to cheat me and make my home a place of unrest.'

Jesus answers, 'Love your enemies. Do good things to those who hate you. Pray for those people who are mean to you and make your life difficult.'

This causes a lot of muttering in the crowd. The people aren't used to this kind of teaching. They have tended to argue with each other, but here, this man is telling them to do good things and pray for people they don't like!

Jesus starts to get annoyed with them. You can see that his face looks cross and he stands up in the middle of them.

'How can you call me Teacher when you don't do what I say?' he says. 'Follow me!'

He gathers up his robes and walks briskly off towards the water's edge. The crowd, muttering and shuffling, get up and follow him.

'Look at this!' Jesus commands. You look over to where he is pointing. There is a man building a house a little way from the lake. He is building it on a rocky outcrop, and it seems to be taking him ages. As you watch, you can see that he has to chip away at the rocks he is building on, to make them flat, before he can put the bricks on to them. It is hot work and he needs to keep stopping for a rest and a drink.

'If you hear my words and change your lives, you are like this man. You will have a firm foundation. If you build your house on solid rock, when the floods come your house will stay standing.'

'But look over this way.'

You look to where Jesus is pointing now. There is another

man building his house. The land around him looks very soft and sandy. He has got much further on; in fact, he is almost ready to put the roof on. He seems very pleased with himself, and he keeps stopping to admire his hard work.

'If you hear what I say and you do not change your ways, you are like this man. When the floods come along, the whole house will be washed away and will fall to the ground.'

The crowd is silent as everyone looks at each of the builders and thinks about what Jesus has said. They think of the things they have to do to change, and gradually a peacefulness comes over them and they start to smile.

Follow-up

Did you enjoy the story? Did you have a good picture in your head? Could you imagine what the builders looked like? Can you think of a time when you had to change what you were doing? Is it easy to change?

As we go round the circle, you can tell us about your picture if you want to.

Prayer

Dear Lord Jesus, there are so many good things that you tried to teach us to do. Help us to listen carefully to your words in the Bible, and to try to do the right thing so that we can learn to be the best that we can be. Thank you. Amen

Senses 9

Get up and walk

 Theme
The gift of movement

 **Bible verses**
Acts 3:1–10

 Artefacts
A pair of shoes or sandals
Dance music
Some background music from the suggested list in Appendix 1
CD player

Introduction

Play the dance music to the children. Talk about what they might expect to do when they hear it.

Show them the shoes. What would they expect to use them for? Think about the things that they couldn't do if they couldn't walk—for example, run, jump, skip, play hopscotch and so on. (Play the background music now.)

Jumping for joy!

Slowly… close your eyes. You are back in Bible times. It is a hot day and you can see a lot of people walking towards the temple. You guess that they must be going there for a service.

There is the sound of a distant bell, telling everyone that it will soon be time to go into the temple. Many of them look hot and tired as the sun beats down on them. Their feet look hot and dusty and uncomfortable. The crowds move slowly as they chatter to their friends. Some have their heads bowed, as if in prayer, and some are carrying expensive-looking books; perhaps they will use these in the temple.

As you look around the people, you recognize two of them. You can see John and Peter, two of Jesus' disciples. They are coming up to one of the temple gates.

This temple gate is really stunning. It has a lot of intricate paintwork decorations around it, and so the locals call it the 'Beautiful Gate'. It has all kinds of bright colours of red, gold and blue in lots of different designs.

At the same time as Peter and John are walking towards the gate, you can see a man being carried. 'Why is he being carried?' you wonder.

Ah, it's a bit clearer now. He has been put down on the ground near the gate and he is holding out his hands, calling to the people who are walking towards the temple.

'Give me your spare money, good travellers. I cannot walk.'

In those days, if you couldn't walk it wasn't very easy to

get a job, so the only way you could get money was to beg for it, and hope that some kind people would give you enough to feed yourself.

Lots of people pass the man and look at him. Then they walk away and carry on talking to their friends. But still, he calls out to the passers-by.

You see Peter and John walk up to the man. He looks straight at them and speaks.

'Give me your spare money, kind men.'

Peter looks at John and then speaks to the man.

'Look at us! We have no possessions, no money and no houses to sleep in. All that we have is given to us. We cannot give you money because we don't have any.'

The man looks more carefully at the two men and his face falls in disappointment as he realizes that they can't give him anything. They look hot and tired and their clothes look worn. They must be right. Perhaps they are no better off than he is.

Then Peter speaks again.

'I don't have any silver or gold, but I will give you what I do have. In the name of Jesus Christ from Nazareth, get up and start walking.'

Then Peter takes the man's right hand and helps him up to his feet. Suddenly, the man's feet and ankles grow strong and he finds that he can walk. Not only that, but he can run and skip and jump! He is the happiest man alive. Now he won't have to beg any more. He will be able to get a job and earn enough money to eat properly.

He thanks Peter and John. He goes into the temple courts and you can see him skipping and jumping and shouting at the top of his voice, 'Praise be to God, for he has made me well!'

The people round about look over to where the noise is coming from.

'Don't I know him?' asks one woman.

'Yes, he looks familiar,' adds another.

'I know who he is,' says the man who is with them. 'He's the beggar who sits by the temple gate.'

'But that can't be right,' says the first woman.

'Yes, that beggar couldn't walk,' adds her friend.

'Well, look at him now,' observes the man. 'He can certainly walk now, and skip and jump.'

'What an amazing thing to have happened,' says the friend. 'Let's follow him into the temple to find out more.'

You watch as the crowd go into the temple. You smile to yourself, because you know what has happened.

Follow-up

Did you enjoy that story? Which parts of it could you picture really clearly in your mind? Could you imagine Peter and John talking to the beggar? Could you hear their voices in your head?

As we go round the circle, think about the parts of the story that you liked. If you want to, you can tell us what you imagined.

Prayer

Dear Father God, thank you for our legs to walk, run, skip and jump with. Thank you that we have the freedom to move when we want to. Help us to remember to thank you for all of the things that we can do. Amen

Saul becomes a follower of Jesus

 Theme
God's greatest gift

 **Bible verses**
Acts 9:1–18

 Artefacts
A simple cross, or a badge with the fish sign on it (see template on p. 146)

Introduction

Talk to the children about people they have heard of or know who believe in Jesus, or who go to church. What sort of things might they do to make them different from other people?

Explain to the children that it was dangerous to believe in Jesus in the years after he died. Followers of Jesus used special secret signs such as the cross or the fish. If people found out that you were a Christian, you could be put in prison or you could be killed.

A man called Saul

Slowly… close your eyes. You are back in Bible times. It is a few years after Jesus died and rose again. There are lots of people who don't like Christians, and who are trying to have them put into prison. One of those men, who is the worst person to be near if you're a Christian, is a man called Saul. Saul is a man with dark hair, who frowns a lot.

You can see Saul. You are glad that he can't see you, as you don't like the look of him much. He is muttering to himself, and you can just hear what he's saying.

'The next Christian I catch, be it man or woman, is going to be thrown in prison. I will take them to the high priests, who will be pleased with me. I'll get rid of everybody that ever believed Jesus was special.'

You can see that he has some other men with him. They don't look very happy. They just seem to be doing what Saul tells them to.

They are all walking along a dusty road. It is the road that leads to a city called Damascus. It's a hot day and the roads are dry. Saul is getting crosser and crosser as he gets hotter and hotter.

Suddenly, he falls to the ground and kneels down. His hands are shielding his face from a bright light in the sky. He is trying to look up but the light is too bright for him. You can hear a voice.

'Saul, Saul, why are you so cruel to me?'

'Who are you?' Saul asks.

'I am Jesus. Now get up and go into the city and you will be told what to do.'

Then, just as suddenly, the bright light disappears and Saul is left kneeling on the ground. The men around Saul look confused. They obviously saw the bright light just like you did, but they didn't hear the voice.

You watch Saul get up slowly, but then you see him trip and stumble. He puts his hands out to break his fall and you hear him say, 'Help me, I can't see!'

The men around him rush forward, take him by the arms and help him to his feet. They lead him by his hand into the city.

Time passes by and you watch Saul. After three days he hasn't eaten or drunk a thing.

Then you see another man in a house near to where Saul is staying. He is called Ananias. He is a man who believes in Jesus, and you can see him on his knees, praying. In his prayer you hear the same voice call out to him that spoke to Saul.

'Ananias, go to the house of Judas on Straight Street. Ask for a man called Saul. He has had a vision that you will make him see again.'

'But Lord,' Ananias answers, 'I have heard about this man. He is dangerous to all who believe in you. He has come here to arrest anyone who believes in you.'

'Don't worry,' Jesus says. 'I have shown him what he must do to help my people.'

You watch as Ananias stands up. His face is pale and he looks scared. This man Saul must be a nasty man to make Ananias so worried.

You watch Ananias walk out of his house and down the road until he gets to Straight Street. He goes to the house where Saul is staying.

Saul is on his knees, praying. He raises his head when he hears Ananias walk into the room.

'Who are you?' Saul asks.

'I am Ananias. The Lord has sent me to you,' Ananias replies. You can hear his voice quivering, as he's obviously really nervous of what Saul might do.

'Peace be with you, Ananias,' Saul replies, and Ananias gently puts his hands on to Saul's eyes. His arms are shaking as he starts to pray.

'Brother Saul, the Lord appeared to you on your way here. He has great plans for you. He has sent me to make you well again.'

As he prays, you can see something fall off Saul's eyes. It looks like the shiny scales that are on a fish.

Then you watch as Saul gets up. He looks at Ananias and smiles and gives him a huge hug.

'Come with me, brother Ananias. We have a lot of work to do. Jesus Christ has shown me that I was wrong, and he will show me how I must tell the whole world about him. From generation to generation, all will know about the Lord, and I will be one of the saints who tells them.'

Saul and Ananias walk out of the house and go up the street. You can just see them as they go, and you can hear them talking as if they have always been best friends.

Follow-up

Did you enjoy the story? Could you picture Saul kneeling down on the road? Could you imagine what Ananias might have looked like?

Talk about how people pray to God and to Jesus. What do these people do to learn about them? Where might they go?

As we go round the circle, you can tell us about some of the things you pictured in your head, if you want to.

Prayer

Dear Lord Jesus, you came into our world to make it a better place, and to make us the best that we can be. Help us to learn about you, and to learn about the people who first believed in you. Help us to listen to the stories and learn to be the people you want us to be. Amen

Part Two

SEASONS

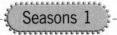

Shepherds and angels

 Theme
Christmas

 Bible verses
Luke 2:8–21

 Artefacts
A soft toy sheep
A picture of sheep and shepherds in Bible times

Introduction

Talk about how people would have to look after sheep in ancient times, and how it was a dangerous job because of the wild animals that would try to attack the sheep.

An amazing sight!

Slowly… close your eyes. You're back in Bible times, and this time you're standing halfway up a hill. You can't see much because it is night time. But you can feel and you can hear. You can feel the wind blowing—I should tie that old coat a bit tighter, if I were you.

Listen hard… yes, that's right. You can hear sheep! There are lots and lots of them, bleating and baa-ing. Just over there—be careful in the dark—you can see a small fire. Round it are other shepherds. Some of them are asleep. You can hear their snores.

If you look away and below for a moment, you can just see the light of some fires in a town. The town is Bethlehem. People who live in Bethlehem own most of the sheep that you are looking after. One of the shepherds comes running up to the others.

'I don't know what it is,' he says, out of breath, 'but the sheep are really restless. I know there have been wolves about.'

'Better keep awake, then,' says another shepherd. 'Don't want to lose any more sheep.'

Just as he says that, the sky gets much lighter. Soon you can see everything—the shepherds and the sheep. An angel hovers in the middle of the light. The angel is bright and shining and dazzles anyone who looks at him.

All the shepherds have fallen to the ground. Everything is

silent. Even the sheep have stopped bleating and baa-ing. Then the angel speaks.

'There's nothing to be frightened about,' he says. 'I've come to bring you some great news! This news will make everyone happy.'

What can this news be? What is it that will make everyone happy?

'Today in Bethlehem,' he continues, 'your Saviour was born. He is Christ the Lord. You will know who he is because you will find him dressed in baby clothes, lying on a bed of hay.'

As if one angel was not enough, suddenly the whole sky seems full of angels. They are singing the most beautiful song.

'Praise God in heaven! Peace on earth to everyone who pleases God.'

They keep singing, and you badly want to join in. Then, as suddenly as they came, they've gone. The sky seems so dark. The shepherds all start talking at once.

'Angels…'

'Hundreds of them…'

'Up here…'

'Never heard such a lovely song…'

'A baby who is…'

'… Christ the Lord…'

'We must go and see him…'

'But,' says the oldest shepherd, 'what about the sheep?'

Someone pokes the fire and a flame burns brightly. All the shepherds are pointing at you.

'*You* can stay with the sheep, while we go down to the town!' they shout.

And that's what happens. Thankfully, no wolves or leopards, hyenas or bears come and steal a sheep while the others are away. At last, just as the dawn is breaking on the eastern hills, you hear them coming back. And they are still singing the angels' song.

'Praise God in heaven! Peace on earth to everyone who pleases God.'

They flop down round the fire. You're bursting with impatience.

'Come on, *tell me!*'

The oldest shepherd looks at the others. They nod.

'We found the baby, just like the angel promised, in a stable,' he says. 'He was there lying in a little old bed of straw. His mum asked why we had come. We told her all about the angels and what they called her baby. She didn't seem too surprised, though.'

'He's a special baby, all right,' said the youngest shepherd. 'He'll be a really special man when he grows up.'

'It all happened just like the angel told us,' they said together.

Follow-up

Talk about the picture you imagined in your head. Which part of the story did you like best? Why? What did the shepherds in your story look like? What did it feel like as you were by the fire, looking down the hill into the town?

How did the shepherds feel after they had seen Jesus?

As we go round the group, if you want to you can tell us about the picture you made in your head. You don't have to say anything if you don't want to.

Prayer

Dear Lord Jesus, thank you for the shepherds, who believed in you and were ready to follow the angels. Thank you that they shared the good news of your birth so that we can learn about it today and celebrate the good news too. Let us also share the good news with our friends so that everybody knows about you. Amen

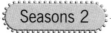

Seasons 2

Special visitors

 Theme
Epiphany

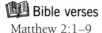 **Bible verses**
Matthew 2:1–9

 Artefacts
A star cut out for each child to hold
One small present, wrapped up, for the children to look at
A picture of a camel
Incense sticks

Introduction

Talk to the children about ways of travelling. Explain how people travelled many years ago. Show the children the picture of a camel and talk about why it was used. Talk about why people make journeys.

Have some incense sticks ready and talk about what they are used for. You may decide to light one so that the children can experience the smell.

Seeing stars

Slowly… close your eyes. In the darkness, imagine that it is night time. But it isn't completely dark because it's a starry night. Look around. You can see hundreds of stars. A few of them are really bright. Look, there's a shooting star tearing across the sky.

Look at the moon. It is yet to grow fully round. The stars seem to be dancing round the moon. Hold your star and feel its shape. Imagine that you can put your star anywhere in the sky. Where will you put it? Look how bright your star has become.

Your star is going on a journey across the sky. Your star has become the Christmas star. Look, there are men gazing up at your star. Can you hear what they are saying? They seem to be talking about a king. What was that? They want to follow your star to see if it leads them to this king.

The men are preparing for their journey. Look, a boy about your age has brought the camels. Camels make such a funny noise. Can you hear them grunting and groaning as they are loaded? What will the men need for their journey? Food, water, clothes to keep them warm at night?

The sun has set and it's beginning to get dark. There's your star again. It moves slowly across the sky. The men are excited. One of them points to your star. Can you see them getting on their camels? There are more groans and grunts.

All through the night, your star guides the men across the

desert. It's really cold now. The men wrap their clothes round tighter. Can you hear them talking? I think they're wondering how much further they have to go.

Now the sun is up above the horizon and they are looking for somewhere to sleep. Can you find them a shady spot? Look, one of the men is giving the camels some food.

Night after night, they follow your star. Then, suddenly, your star stops over a town. I think that the town is called Bethlehem. How do the men feel now that your star has stopped? Are they excited?

Watch carefully. They've jumped down from their camels. They seem to be looking in those big bags they brought with them. Can you see what they're holding? It looks as though they've brought some presents. I wonder who for? The sun catches one of the presents. Gracious me! It looks like gold. There are two more gifts. Can you smell them? One is called myrrh and the other is called frankincense. They are very precious perfumes.

The men seem to be very excited. Do you think they've found the king they've travelled all these miles to see? Do you think those strange presents are for him? Let's see what they do with them.

They aren't going into a palace. It looks more like a sort of stable. Surely there won't be a king in there! What can you see in the stable? Are there some animals? Which animals can you see in the stable? A baby—yes, there's a baby lying in some warm straw. And the men are kneeling down in front of the baby. What are they doing with their presents? That must be a very special baby.

Your star has done its work. It led the wise men to visit

Jesus, the baby king. Take it down from the sky and hold it in your hand again.

Follow-up

Think about the picture you made in your head. Can you tell us which part of the story you liked best? Why? Did you decide what colours the clothes were that the men in your story were wearing?

Which animals did you see in the stable? Was there anything else in your stable?

As we go round the group, if you want to you can tell us about the picture you made in your head. You don't have to say anything if you don't want to.

Prayer

Dear Father God, thank you for the special story of Jesus' birth. Thank you for the men who followed the star to the stable and brought their precious gifts. May we remember those gifts that the baby Jesus had as we get closer to Christmas, and thank you that we also have people who love us and give us presents. Amen

A special meeting

 Theme
Thanksgiving for the birth of a baby

 Bible verses
Luke 2:22–38

 Artefact
Photograph of a newborn baby

Introduction

Have ready a few examples of items that might be given to celebrate the birth of a baby, such as a baby journal, silverware or special china. Show photographs of a newborn baby and talk about how people feel when a new baby is born into a family.

A thanksgiving service is a common occurrence nowadays, and some parents choose to celebrate the birth of their baby in this way, leaving the baptism until a later date when the child is able to decide for himself or herself. If this is the case, the child may receive his or her name at the thanksgiving service. It may be possible to invite a local minister to come and talk (on a separate occasion) about a service of thanksgiving for the birth of a baby.

The very young and the very old

Slowly… close your eyes. We are travelling back today to the temple in Jerusalem. It is a huge building and full of people. Look over there—that's Mary and Joseph. Mary is carrying a baby. It must be Jesus. Let's follow them and see what happens.

Mary and Joseph show Jesus to one of the priests in the temple, and Jesus receives his name. Do you remember how the angel came to Mary to tell her she was going to have a very special baby? He told her then that her son would be called Jesus. It is all happening as the angel promised.

Some time after Jesus receives his name, his parents are back in the temple again. Let's watch and see what happens this time. Joseph is carrying two doves, which he has just handed to the priest. This is the traditional way of saying 'thank you' to God for the safe birth of their firstborn son.

Look over there. Can you see that old man? He's rather bent and stooped, but he's got a kind and gentle face. His name is Simeon. What is he doing now? He has taken the baby Jesus from Mary and is holding him in his arms. Simeon looks so happy to see Jesus. He seems to be saying 'thank you' to God for Jesus.

If we tiptoe a little closer—careful, don't make a noise—then we might hear what Simeon is saying.

'Lord, I am your servant, and now I can die in peace, because you have kept your promise to me. With my own eyes I have seen what you have done to save your people.'

Simeon finishes his prayer and gives Jesus back to Mary and Joseph. They seem very surprised at what Simeon has just said. Quick, listen again.

'May the Lord bless you. This child of yours is a sign from God. Some will believe in him and follow him. Others will want nothing to do with him.'

Mary looks a bit puzzled at this. Old Simeon is walking slowly away, but there is a spring in his step that wasn't there before. He has been waiting all his life for Jesus to come. God promised him he would not die until he saw Jesus, and God always keeps his promises.

As Simeon disappears out of sight, back to his home in Jerusalem, someone else is coming. You can just see her through the shadows in the temple. It is another older person. If anything, she seems to be even older than Simeon. Her name is Anna and she is 84 years old. Everyone in the temple knows Anna; she is there every day. She spends nights and days praying and worshipping God.

Anna has come over to Mary and the baby. The extra-ordinary thing is that Anna seems to know exactly who Jesus is. She keeps stopping people and telling them about the baby. Like Simeon, she is giving thanks to God for letting her see Jesus.

Lots of the people in Israel are angry that the Roman soldiers live in their country and order them what to do. Many want to fight the Romans and drive them out. But others, like Simeon and Anna, know that that isn't God's way. They spend their lives in patient prayer, waiting for God. So when God came in Jesus, they knew at once who he was.

Simeon and Anna and others like them have a lovely name. They are called 'The Quiet in the Land'. I don't think we have many of those at school!

Now that Mary and Joseph have done what the law tells them to do for their baby, they are leaving Jerusalem and returning to Nazareth. That's where Jesus will grow up, learn to be a carpenter like Joseph, and then do the work God his Father sent him to do. As Mary, Joseph and the baby leave the temple, we must do the same.

Follow-up

Did you imagine what Simeon and Anna looked like? Were they bent over or did they have walking sticks to lean on? Did they have kind faces?

Can you imagine why Mary and Joseph thought Simeon's and Anna's reactions were a bit strange when they saw Jesus? If you want to, you can share some of your ideas.

Prayer

Dear Father God, thank you for the patient people who wait for you to work in their lives. Thank you that they show us that you keep your promises. Help us to learn how to be patient people too. Amen

Jesus enters Jerusalem

 Theme
Palm Sunday

 Bible verses
Luke 19:28–40

 Artefacts
Palm crosses (enough for everyone in the class)
A picture of Jesus sitting on a donkey

Introduction

How would you travel if you lived when Jesus lived and had to go on a journey? The most likely way would be either on foot or on a donkey. Very few people rode horses. Our story today is about how a friend of Jesus lent him a donkey—and what happened when Jesus rode it.

A special journey

Slowly… close your eyes. You've been walking for some time along a very hot and dusty road. Just ahead of you is the village called Bethany. Beyond that, not far now, is the great city of Jerusalem. Can you see how the dust falls off when you shake yourself?

A whole group of friends have been walking with Jesus towards Jerusalem. Jesus stops as he comes to the first houses in the village. He beckons you and one of the others.

'Go,' he says, 'into the village ahead of you. There you'll find a young donkey tied to a post. Untie the donkey and bring it back to me.'

'But Jesus,' you say, feeling rather worried, 'what happens if the owner asks what we're doing?'

'Then,' said Jesus, 'tell them that the Master needs it.'

It's amazing, isn't it, how Jesus has friends in so many different places? But of course he's right. Just down the road, tied to a post, are a donkey and her foal. A rather large and fierce-looking man is giving them a drink.

'I hope he understands,' you whisper to your friend. 'We don't want to be caught donkey stealing.'

'You can do the talking!' he says.

The owner of the donkeys has gone off, but just as you start to untie the animal, he comes running back—looking even fiercer.

'Why are you untying my donkey?' he asks crossly.

'The Master needs it!' you stutter.

The man's face changes at once. Suddenly there is a big smile. He hands you the rope tied round the foal's neck and pats the little donkey as you lead it away.

Jesus is waiting outside the village. Some of his other friends throw a cloak over the donkey's back and Jesus gets on. As this happens, large crowds begin to gather by the side of the road. They start throwing their cloaks on the road and tearing palm branches from the trees. Do you think the little donkey might be frightened by all this?

As the road leads up towards Jerusalem, the crowds gets even larger and even noisier. They seem to be praising God. Can you hear the words they're using?

'God bless the king.'

'He comes in the name of the Lord.'

'Peace in heaven and glory to God.'

People on either side of the road are waving their palm branches in the air, shouting and singing. Everyone seems to be joining in. No, look over there—not everyone is happy. Jesus is just passing a group of Pharisees. They're very stern and strict. You can see from their faces that they don't like what's going on.

'Teacher,' they shout above the crowd, 'make your followers stop shouting.'

Jesus says a funny thing.

'If they keep quiet, the stones in the road will start shouting.'

Jesus knows that nothing is going to stop the happiness of the day—not even the grumbling Pharisees.

As Jesus gets closer to the city, you can see the sun shining on the temple. He has got off the donkey. As he stares at the city, you quietly lead the donkey back down the road to Bethany. The donkey has done his job—and so have you. You hand the foal back to his owner.

'The Master says, "Thank you",' you tell him.

Follow-up

How did you feel when Jesus chose you to do a job for him? Did it make you feel important? What did you feel like when the donkey's owner asked what you were doing? Were you worried?

Can you picture what the crowds must have looked like as they waved their palm tree branches and cheered? Can you imagine how noisy it must have been?

As we go round the group, if you want to you can tell us about the picture you made in your head. You don't have to say anything if you don't want to.

Prayer

Dear Father God, thank you for all the people who gathered to see Jesus. Thank you that they believed in him, and that they celebrated all that he did. Help us to learn about him so that we too can celebrate for ourselves. Amen

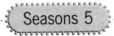

Jesus washes his disciples' feet

 Theme

Holy Week: Special days

Bible verses

John 13:1–13 and Luke 22:14–20

Artefacts

A basin of water and a towel

Seder picture, bread and wine, unleavened bread, and a Seder plate with the different parts of the meal by it

Introduction

Every year we remember certain days—birthdays, Christmas, Easter, harvest and lots more. One of the special days for Jesus and his friends was the festival of Passover. Just as we remember the birth of Jesus at Christmas, so at Passover the people of Israel remembered how God led them out of Egypt, where for years they had been slaves. Passover was, and still is, always celebrated with a special meal called Seder.

Master and servant

Slowly… close your eyes. Today we find ourselves with thousands of people in the city of Jerusalem. They've all come to Jerusalem for the Passover. Can you hear all the different languages they're speaking? Greek, Aramaic, Hebrew, Arabic and—over there—some Roman soldiers speaking Latin.

There is pushing and shoving, animals being driven through the streets, soldiers marching, children crying. Look, just over there is Jesus and his friends. Let's try to hear what he's saying. Push your way through the crowd.

'Peter and John,' Jesus says, 'I want you to get the Passover meal ready for us.'

'But where?' asks Peter. 'Where do you want us to prepare it?'

That's a very good question. Lots of people are trying to find a place for their Seder meal. But Jesus has already thought about it.

'In the city you will see a man carrying a jar of water,' says Jesus. 'Follow him to his house. Tell the owner that your teacher wants to know where he and his friends can eat the Passover meal. The owner will take you upstairs and show you the room.'

That's a sort of secret sign for Peter and John. They are able to find their man in the crowd because usually only women carry water jars. Peter and John go off to prepare the meal and we follow with Jesus and the others a little later.

After the brilliant sunshine outside, it seems quite dark in the upstairs room. Jesus and his friends are there around the table. They have eaten the Seder meal and remembered how God set their ancestors free in Egypt. Now something rather unexpected seems to be happening.

Look, Jesus has stood up. He's picked up a towel and wrapped it round his waist. Can you guess what he's going to do? Now he's pouring water into a basin. He is going to each of his friends and—yes, that's right—very carefully and lovingly he is washing everyone's feet. That's not a pleasant thing to do. The roads are dusty and people's feet get very dirty.

Some of his friends look very surprised—especially Peter.

Now Jesus has sat down again. Let's listen to what he says.

'Do you understand what I have done? If I, your Lord and Teacher, have washed your feet, you should do the same for each other.'

All his friends are quiet. They are thinking about what he has just told them. What do you think it means? Perhaps it means that no one is more important than anyone else.

Now Jesus has picked up some bread from the table. He gives thanks to God and passes the bread to his neighbour.

'This is my body, which is given for you,' he says. 'Eat this as a way of remembering me.'

Look, Jesus has taken a cup of wine in his hand. I think he is going to share it with the others.

'This is my blood, which is poured out for you,' he says. 'Drink this and remember me.'

It's time we left Jesus and his friends in the upstairs room. They are looking very sad at some of the things he has been saying to them. I don't think they will stay there much longer. Perhaps we'll find out what happens another time.

Follow-up

Did you feel worried by all the different people in the crowds, pushing and shoving? Could you imagine what some of the people might have looked like?

Did you think it was a strange thing to do when Jesus washed his friends' feet? Would you like to do that? Could you picture what it might have looked like with Jesus and his friends all sharing the same meal around the table?

Prayer

Dear Lord Jesus, even at a sad time in your life you still had important things to tell us. You told us that we must all look after each other and treat each other kindly. Help us to remember what you have taught us, even when things aren't going well, and help us to be kind and caring to each other. Amen

Seasons 6

Jesus is arrested

 Theme
Holy Week: Peter says he doesn't know Jesus

 Bible verses
Mark 14:66–72

 Artefacts
A picture of a garden
A bugle (or a picture of one)

Introduction

After Jesus and his friends finished their Passover meal, they went out of Jerusalem to a quiet garden called Gethsemane. As they walked through the garden, Jesus began to tell his friends what was going to happen to him. 'All of you,' he said, 'will leave me. You will say you never knew me.'

Peter was upset by this. 'Even if all the others reject you, I never will.' Jesus looked at Peter. 'Tonight, before the cock crows twice, you will say three times that you don't know me.' Peter was so sure of himself that he said, 'I will never say I don't know you!'

Now are you ready to travel back to Jerusalem?

When the bugle sounds

Slowly… close your eyes. We are in the courtyard of a very large house. Although it is the middle of the night, we can see clearly what's happening, as there are plenty of oil lamps and a small open fire.

There seem to be a lot of people coming and going. Do you see who that is, warming his hands by the fire? Yes, that's right, it's Peter. You can just catch a glimpse of Jesus in the house. He was arrested in the garden and brought here by the religious leaders. They are asking Jesus lots of questions.

Listen, I think Peter is being asked a question too. One of the women who works for the high priest has gone over to the fire and is staring at Peter.

'I know you,' she says. 'You were with that Jesus from Nazareth.'

Oh dear, it looks as though Peter has been found out. Will the soldiers arrest him too? Peter stands up and shakes his head.

'That just isn't true!' he shouts. 'I don't know what you're talking about. I've no idea what you mean.'

Peter walks away from the fire and stands by the entrance to the courtyard. At that moment a bugle note sounds over the city. That made you jump! It is three o'clock in the morning, the time the Roman guard is changed. The Romans call the bugle call the *gallicinium*, which is Latin for 'cock crow'. Do you think Peter has remembered what Jesus said?

But the woman hasn't finished with Peter. She points to him again.

'This man is one of them!' she says.

'No, I'm not!' shouts Peter.

But some of the crowd come away from the fire and surround him.

'You are one of Jesus' friends,' says one of them. 'I'd know that accent anywhere—you're from Galilee.'

Peter curses and swears, 'I don't even know the man you're talking about!'

Look, can you see? A door has opened. Out come some of the religious leaders and the soldiers. The soldiers are taking Jesus through the courtyard. Just for a moment Jesus turns his face and looks at Peter.

And the bugle call sounds again. Can you see Peter's face? He's holding his head in his hands. Tears are running down his cheeks. Yes, now he's remembered what Jesus told him. 'Before the cock crows twice, you will say three times that you don't know me.'

The people who have been speaking to Peter look away as Jesus is led out by the soldiers. Now is Peter's chance to leave. There he goes—a very unhappy man. It's time we left as well, but I'm glad to say that the story doesn't end there. We shall see Peter again, and by then everything will be better.

Follow-up

What did the woman in your picture look like? Was she a friendly person?

As we go round the group, if you want to you can tell us about the picture you made in your head. You don't have to say anything if you don't want to.

Prayer

Dear Lord Jesus, sometimes it isn't easy to admit that we know about you. Sometimes we're worried about what other people might say. Thank you that you understand and that you still love us even when we don't do the right thing. Help us to learn how to follow you and to be the people you want us to be. Amen

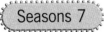

New life

 Theme

The story of Easter Day

📖 **Bible verses**

John 20:11–18

◎ **Artefact**

A simple Easter garden made from a Fruit Corners yoghurt pot. (Wash the pot and bend the smaller section up to form the tomb. Fill the larger section with soil and arrange some miniature plants, a little moss and a few small stones on the soil to make the garden.) Alternatively, show a picture of the garden tomb.

Introduction

Last time, we heard how Jesus was arrested and taken to the religious leaders. In the courtyard of the high priest's house, Peter, Jesus' friend, told everyone he didn't know Jesus.

The leaders wanted to get rid of Jesus, and he was put to death on the day we call Good Friday. Think for a moment about how his friends must have felt when they knew Jesus was dead. They had been with him for three years. He had taught them. They believed him to be a very special person—and now he was dead. Had they made a mistake? Was Jesus just an ordinary person after all?

One of Jesus' friends was a woman called Mary. She came from the village of Magdala near the western side of Lake Galilee. She had been very ill but Jesus had cured her. No wonder she loved him.

Two days have passed and it is now very early on Sunday morning.

A cause for a celebration

Slowly… close your eyes. We are standing in a garden on the outskirts of Jerusalem. Even though it is still quite dark, we can see the outline of a cave in the hillside. It was in this cave that the body of Jesus was laid. A huge stone was rolled over the entrance to stop people getting in.

Listen a moment… I think someone is coming. Yes, look! You can just see a woman walking slowly up to the cave. She's stopped. She looks shocked. Her mouth is open wide and she is staring at the cave. Someone has rolled the stone away and the entrance to the cave is open. Mary—because that is who it is—turns and runs away.

Back in the city of Jerusalem, two of Jesus' friends are very surprised when Mary comes running up to them. When she gets her breath back, she blurts it all out.

'I've been to the cave. It is empty—they have taken Jesus away. We don't know where they've put him.'

Without waiting to hear any more, Peter and John leave Mary there and race each other back to the cave. To start with, they run side by side but soon John begins to overtake Peter. He is first there. Do you see? John is standing outside the cave looking in.

Now Peter comes and barges past John, right into the cave. Lying there is the cloth that was wrapped round the body of Jesus. Now John has joined Peter inside.

They are both smiling—it looks like good news.

'We must tell the others,' shouts Peter. Off they go again, back to the city. It is light now. The sun is up and we are going to stay here and find out if anything else happens.

Look, through the olive trees, we can see Mary again. She must have come a different way from Peter and John. She doesn't know what they found out. Poor Mary looks very sad. She is beginning to cry.

She ducks her head to look into the cave. Sitting on the rock shelf, where the body of Jesus had been, are two angels. They speak to Mary.

'Why are you crying?'

'They've taken away my Lord's body! I don't know where they have put him.'

We can see what Mary cannot. Someone has walked up to the cave. I can hardly believe it! It's Jesus. It really is. He speaks to Mary.

'Why are you crying? Who are you looking for?'

Poor Mary is crying so hard, she can't see anything.

'Sir,' she says, 'if you have taken his body away, please tell me where he is.'

Jesus just speaks one word. 'Mary,' he says.

This one word is more than enough. The look on Mary's face is amazing. It changes from tears to smiles in an instant.

Jesus, who was dead, is alive again, and Mary is so happy that she wants to hug him. The smile on Mary's face is almost brighter than the sun.

Jesus tells Mary to go and let all his other friends know that she has seen him—that he is alive again. This time, Mary almost dances out of the garden, through the city streets, to tell the others. Soon all his other friends will see Jesus too.

Follow-up

Stay with your eyes closed for just a minute longer. Can you imagine what the friends of Jesus did when Mary told them the good news? Did they have a party? Did they all believe it? Did some think they couldn't believe it until they saw Jesus for themselves?

Prayer

Dear Lord Jesus, Mary, Peter and John were so happy when they realized that you were alive again. Help us to share some of that joy when we hear the story of Easter Day. Help us to learn more and more about you and to get to know you better. Amen

Seasons 8

The breakfast on the beach

 Theme
After Easter: Jesus and Peter

 Bible verses
John 21:1–19

 Artefact
A piece of netting to represent the fishing net, or some fish shapes cut from shiny paper

Introduction

Jesus met with his friends several times after his meeting with Mary on Easter Day. But there was one special meeting that Jesus had with Peter. When Jesus was arrested, Peter had said three times that he did not know Jesus. Later, after the events of Easter Day, Peter said to his friends, 'I'm going fishing.' Six of the others said they would come too.

A true friend

Slowly… close your eyes. Imagine that, once again, we are standing by the side of Lake Galilee. It's very early in the morning. The sun is just rising above the mountain tops and beginning to shine on the lake.

Can you see the fishing boat? It's about a hundred metres from the shore. Look at the fishermen. Do they look as though they've caught any fish? I don't think so. They've been out on the lake all night. By now they are hungry and cold and having a moan about empty nets.

Suddenly they hear a voice. Over there, just along the shoreline, is a man. He seems to be shouting something to the fishermen. His voice carries easily over the water at this time of the day. It's the usual question—the one every fisherman gets asked. Can you guess what it is? Yes, that's right. 'Have you caught anything?' The fishermen shout back, 'No!'

Then the man shouts again. 'Let your net down on the right side of the boat, and you will catch some fish!'

Do you think they will take any notice of a stranger? Yes, they've thrown the net out of the boat. Gracious me, can you see what's happening? The water round the net is bubbling. There are hundreds of fish.

Peter and all the others have rushed to one side of the boat. I hope they don't tip it over. They are struggling to pull in the net. Fish are spilling out. They are everywhere. I don't think they will be able to drag the net into the boat—it's too heavy.

John has taken his eyes off the fish for a moment and looks towards the shore. Suddenly he recognizes the man on the shore.

Can you hear what he said? 'It's the Lord!'

What was that splash? Oh no, it's Peter. He's jumped in. He's half swimming and half walking towards the shore. Let's watch and see what happens. Peter is splashing his way to the beach. The other friends are rowing as hard as they can to bring the boat, full of fish, to the shore. I wonder who will win? Well, I think it was a dead heat. Peter's gone back to the boat to get the fish.

Oh, what a wonderful smell! Jesus has lit a small fire and is cooking the fish over it. Those friends of his must be starving after being on the lake all night. They are warming their hands round the fire and eating the fish. Good job there are plenty. I wouldn't mind some myself.

At last they've had enough. What a lovely thing for Jesus to do—cook breakfast for his friends. Some of them are stretching out on the sand and falling asleep in the warm sun. I don't blame them, after being up all night on the lake.

But Peter is still awake. I think Jesus wants to speak to him. Let's get a bit nearer and try to hear what Jesus is saying. That's strange; Jesus is calling him by his old name, which is Simon.

'Simon, do you love me?'

Poor Peter—or should I say Simon—looks very unhappy.

'Yes, Lord, you know that I love you.' The words come tumbling out. Peter keeps his eyes on the fire.

Then Jesus asks him the same question again.

'Simon, do you love me?'

Peter looks puzzled. Surely Jesus knows that he loves him. But he answers as before. 'Yes, Lord, you know that I love you.'

Then Jesus asks the same question for the third time.

'Simon, do you love me?'

Poor Peter is looking very upset. There are tears in his eyes. He is looking so sad. 'Lord, you know everything. You know that I love you!'

Then Jesus says just two words to Peter: 'Follow me.' And suddenly a smile breaks out on Peter's face.

Do you know what I think? Do you remember when Jesus was arrested? He was taken to the religious leaders and Peter followed him from a distance. Peter joined the servants round the fire to warm his hands. One of them recognized him as a friend of Jesus. But Peter shouted out, 'No, I'm not.' Can you remember how often this happened? That's right, Peter said he didn't know Jesus three times.

Now Peter is sitting round another fire. This time it is Jesus asking the questions—the same question three times. This time Peter says, 'Yes, Jesus, I really do love you.'

It is Jesus' way of saying he has forgiven Peter. It is Jesus' way of saying he trusts Peter. He trusts Peter so much that he gives him a job. 'Follow me.'

Follow-up

Could you imagine what the fish smelt like, cooking on the fire? Did it make you feel hungry?

Did you have a picture in your head of Peter splashing through the water to get to Jesus? Did you think it was important for Peter to know that he was a special friend of Jesus?

As we go round the circle, share some of your ideas about the story if you want to, or you could tell the other children about a special friend you have.

Prayer

Dear Lord Jesus, you showed us the true value of good friends. You showed us how to help each other in the good times as well as the difficult ones. Teach us how to remember all that we know about being good friends to each other. Amen

Spreading the word

 Theme
Pentecost: The coming of the Holy Spirit

Bible verses
Acts 2:1–47 (Acts 1:4)

Artefacts
A single candle, or some tealights
A picture of a large crowd

Introduction

On the day we call Ascension Day, Jesus' friends had seen him return to be with his Father in heaven. Before Jesus left them, he told them to stay in Jerusalem. 'Wait here for the Father to give you the Holy Spirit, just as I told you he has promised to do,' he said. So there, in a house in Jerusalem, his friends were expecting something wonderful to happen.

A strange wind

Slowly… close your eyes. Imagine that we are in a large room. There are many people in the room. We know some of them. Walking up and down is Peter, impatient as ever. Trying to calm him down is John. Everyone is talking about Jesus and the promise he made.

Suddenly there is the sound of a strong wind blowing round the house. The talking stops. No one can be heard above the noise of the wind. It seems to fill the whole house.

Look! Now there are tongues of fire moving around the room. A flame has settled on each person in the room. But this flame doesn't burn—it is the flame of the Holy Spirit.

Now everyone is talking again, but all in different languages.

See, through the open door, a huge crowd is gathering outside the house. They have heard the noise of the wind and come to see what is happening. Look at the crowd. They are getting really excited. I think I understand why. Although they have come from many different countries, they can all understand what Jesus' friends are saying.

Listen to them: 'We all hear these men using our own languages to tell the wonderful things God has done.' But one or two of the crowd are making fun of Peter and the others. Can you hear what they are saying? 'They are drunk!'

Peter has gone to the doorway. I think he is going to speak to the crowd.

'Friends and everyone living in Jerusalem, listen carefully to what I have to say. You are wrong to think that we are drunk. After all, it is only nine o'clock in the morning. What you have seen and heard is what God promised would happen.'

The crowd has gone silent. They seem to understand that Peter is saying something very important. He starts by telling them that God promised long ago that the Holy Spirit would come. Then he tells them that God sent Jesus into the world. God knew that Jesus would be put to death, but Jesus was stronger than death.

Now Peter is reminding them about their great ancestor David. He finishes by telling the crowd that everyone should know that Jesus was God, even though he was put to death.

Look at the crowd. They seem very upset by what Peter has told them. They are looking at Peter and asking a question. Can you hear what they are saying? They are asking, 'Friends, what should we do?'

And Peter has an answer for them. 'Turn back to God. Be baptized. Then you too will be given the Holy Spirit.'

What do you think will happen now? There are hundreds of people here. Some are asking to be baptized. No, not some—it must be thousands. All these people have joined Jesus' friends. They have believed what Peter told them and become followers of Jesus. It is quite amazing, but perhaps that's what happens when the Holy Spirit comes.

Let's follow them for another few days. Those first friends of Jesus are teaching groups of people about him. They are sharing what he taught them. They are meeting together in homes and sharing meals. They are doing what Jesus showed his friends to do in that upstairs room before he died—breaking bread together.

It's almost like one big joyful family. Everyone seems so happy. I think it is time we left these new followers of Jesus in Jerusalem.

Follow-up

Could you imagine a picture in your head when you heard the story? Did you imagine what the disciples looked like with the fire above their heads? Can you imagine all the noise of the wind? Do you think it would have been noisy with everyone talking in different languages?

If you want to, you could share some of your ideas.

Prayer

Dear Father God, you sent your Holy Spirit to be with us and to move us in ways that we might not expect. Help us to listen to what you are telling us when we pray to you. Amen

Seasons 10

A story about a farmer

Theme
Harvest

Bible verses
Matthew 13:1–9

Artefacts
Corn or seed: give a few grains of corn or a few seeds to each child. Or show a picture of farming in the Holy Land at the time of Jesus

Introduction

Being a farmer at the time of Jesus was very different from today. Before seeds could be sown, the farmer had to break up the soil. He used a simple wooden plough, which was drawn by oxen. Most of the land in Israel is very rocky and it was hard work to break up the soil and leave it ready for the seed to be sown. There were no machines, no tractors and no combine harvesters.

The farmer sowed the seed by hand. He would take a handful of seed and throw it on the land. This was called 'broadcasting' the seed. Feel the seeds in your hand. Can you imagine walking across a ploughed field, throwing them on the land?

One reason why the crowds loved to hear Jesus speak was

because he told wonderful stories. The stories that he told were always about everyday life. They started with things that the crowd knew and understood. He told a story about a boy who ran away from home and spent all his money. He told a story about a man who went on a journey and got mugged. He told another story about a sheep who got lost on the hillside.

Today the story is about a farmer and the seed.

Seeds and weeds and deeds

Slowly… close your eyes. Today we are going on a journey to Lake Galilee. Standing by the edge of this large lake is a huge crowd of people. We are going to join them. You may need to push your way into the crowd, as there are so many people. Remember to say 'Excuse me, please.'

Can you hear them talking? They seem to be waiting for somebody. The talk gets louder—there's a cheer.

At last, there is a gap in the crowd and a man walks through it. The people know who this is. It is the man they have been waiting for. Can you guess who it might be? Yes, you are right, it is Jesus.

To everyone's surprise, he does not stop at the water's edge. He climbs on board a boat, which pulls out from the shore. The boat stops a short distance away from land. Look, Jesus is sitting down on the boat. The crowd are waiting impatiently. I wonder what he will talk about today.

If you stretch up tall and look behind the crowd, you can

see that a field rises up away from the lake. There's a farmer in the field. He has a bag slung over his shoulder. He dips his hand into the bag and brings it out full of seed. He walks up and down, throwing the seed on to the land.

Look, some of the seed is blowing in the wind. It doesn't all fall in the earth. Some of it is blown on to the rocks and on to the path.

Suddenly the crowd has gone silent. Jesus is speaking. He knows that from the boat the sound of his voice will carry to everyone. And it does—everyone can hear him speaking clearly.

'One day,' says Jesus, 'a farmer went out to sow his corn. He had prepared the ground very well. His oxen and the plough had broken it up. With his seed bag slung over his shoulder, the farmer walked up and down his field. As the farmer scattered the seed, some of it fell on a path.'

There's a murmur of sympathy in the crowd. They've all seen that happen. 'It only takes a little breeze,' says your neighbour, 'and you can waste a lot of seed.' Some of the other people in the crowd tell him to be quiet and listen to what Jesus is saying.

'No sooner had the seed fallen on the path than the birds came and ate it all up,' Jesus continues.

'Greedy little devils,' mutters your neighbour. 'I don't know how they spot it so quickly.'

'Some of the seed fell on rocky ground,' says Jesus. 'There was very little soil on the rocky ground. The seeds soon sprouted in the shallow earth. But you know what happened, from your own experience—as soon as the sun got up, the plants were scorched and died. They had no roots.'

'That happened to me last week,' mutters our friendly neighbour. 'I lost a whole lot of plants. They were no good at all. I've got terrible soil in my field.'

'By the side of the farmer's field were some thorn bushes,' says Jesus. 'Some of the seed fell by the thorns—but when the thorns grew up, they choked the little shoots.'

This time our neighbour has nothing to say. He is waiting to hear how Jesus ends the story.

'But some seed falls into good ground,' says Jesus, 'and the plants grow and produce large heads of corn.'

'That's what I like about the stories Jesus tells,' says our neighbour. 'They always have a good ending!'

Follow-up

When you imagined your story, could you feel what it would have been like to be in a big crowd, trying to hear what Jesus had to say? What did your neighbour look like? Was he a tall or a short man?

Did you imagine what the birds looked like as they were pecking at the seed? Could you imagine what the plants looked like as they were trying to grow among the weeds?

As we go round the group, if you want to you can tell us about the picture you made in your head. You don't have to say anything if you don't want to.

Prayer

Dear Jesus, thank you for the stories you told us to help us to learn about God. Help us to be like the seeds that fell on the good ground. Help us to listen to what you have to say, so that we may grow tall and strong and grow into the good people that you want us to become. Amen

Part Three

FEELINGS

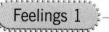

Feelings 1

The wasteful son

 Theme
Knowing forgiveness

 Bible verses
Luke 15:11–31

 Artefacts
A bag of coins
Some ornamental pigs (plastic, china, or soft toys)

Introduction

Jesus often used stories to teach people about God. These stories were about everyday things, so people could understand and imagine what was happening. But there was always a deeper meaning to the story. It was a meaning that helped them and us to understand more about the love of God. This story is about a father and his two sons.

And Dad was there waiting for me

Slowly... close your eyes. We are travelling back to Bible times. Look, just over there is a big house. I think it must be a farmhouse. In front of the house, there is a field of barley, and next to it wheat is beginning to show through the soil.

Can you hear the animals? On that poorer ground, there are sheep and goats. In another field, oxen are pulling the plough through the rocky ground—no tractors here!

The young man holding the plough looks rather fed up. It must be hard work. Now he has left the oxen and sat down in the shade of those trees. He has his head in his hands. He is thinking hard about something.

Now he's got up and run over to an older man, who has been checking that the water is flowing freely in the stream. Can you hear what they are saying?

'Father,' says the young man, 'I've had enough of farming. I'm fed up with ploughing and sowing and feeding the animals and having to get up before the sun. Please give me my share of the farm now. It's time I left home.'

His father looks very sad, but he doesn't argue with his son. They are going into the house to sort it all out. Do you think the boy will have his own way? Do you think he will leave his home and his family? Well, it looks as though we are going to get an answer.

It's taken a few days to make all the arrangements, but now both father and son are standing by the front door. The son has a bag in his hand. He is saying 'goodbye' to his father and off he goes. We will catch up with him later. But what about the father? Can you see how sad he looks to see his son go?

We must be quick to catch up with the boy. Now we are well away from the farm. Look around you. There are buildings and busy streets, and lots of people and markets, and shops and animals and *noise*. It's a good-sized town— very different from the quiet fields.

There he is. Gracious me, how he's changed. Can you see the clothes he's wearing? And those shoes! And that hat! They must have cost a lot of money. He isn't a farm worker any more.

Oh, look, he seems to have made some friends. At least, I hope they are friends. I'm afraid to say that all they seem to want to do is to help him spend his money!

Weeks later, he is still spending his money on anything that takes his fancy—more clothes, the best hotel, and the best places to eat. Ah, look more closely. That fat wallet is very thin. I don't think there's much money left. No, he has just been thrown out of the hotel because he can't pay the bill!

Now there's trouble. All his so-called friends have gone. They don't want to know him now that he's not paying. After two nights sleeping on the streets, he's beginning to look very hungry.

What can he do? He's only good at farm work. Perhaps he will try to get a job on a farm. Let's follow him out into the countryside. Yes, he's knocking at a farmhouse door.

'Pigs,' says the farmer. 'I need someone to feed my pigs.'

'Haven't you got anything else?' begs the boy.

'No, it's pigs or nothing!'

What a come-down! One day spending his money on fine things, and only days later feeding the pigs. He looks so hungry, I think he's going to eat the bean pods that the pigs are eating. He is sitting by the pigs with his head in his hands. Wasn't this how his adventure started? Now he has stood up and started to walk away from the farm.

Did you hear what he said? 'My father's workers have plenty to eat, and here I am, starving to death. I will go home to my father and tell him how wrong I have been. Perhaps he will give me a job on the farm.'

It's a slow journey home. The boy is very tired and very hungry. It's a long walk. So we'll leave him on the road and go back to his father and the farm.

Every day, as the sun rises, the boy's dad has been getting up and walking to farm gate. He stares down the road. Even though his son took his money and ran away, he still misses him.

What is happening now? The father has tucked his robe into his belt and is running as fast as he can down the road. There's a figure stumbling along the road. You can just see him through the dust. It must be the boy.

His father rushes up to him. The boy tries to kneel to say sorry, but his dad flings his arms round him and gives him a huge hug and a kiss.

At last, the boy finds the words. 'Father, I have sinned against God and against you. I am no longer good enough to be called your son.'

Well, it's time to leave them—the son who ran away and

the father who welcomed him home. Can you hear that music? I think there must be a party!

Follow-up

How do you think the father would have felt when his son told him he wanted to leave home? What do you think it must have been like for the son to be able to spend lots of money on things he enjoyed?

How would the son have felt when all the money ran out and he had to work with the pigs? How do you think he felt as he walked home?

Prayer

Dear Father God, sometimes we do silly things and we only think of ourselves. We might have great fun but we don't consider how other people are feeling. Help us to learn how to think of others and to be more responsible people. Amen

Feelings

The lost sheep

 Theme
Being lost and found

 Bible verses
Luke 15:3–7

 Artefact
A sheep puppet or soft toy

Introduction

Can you remember a time when you felt lost? Perhaps you had wandered off in a supermarket, looking for sweets or ice cream. Perhaps you were on a beach when you had found someone else to play with. You might even have been walking through a wood when you were hidden by the trees. Can anyone tell me about a time when they felt lost? It can be quite frightening feeling lost. But the one thing you knew was that someone was looking for you.

Jesus told three stories about being lost and found. One was about a silver coin, one was about a son, and one was about a sheep. Like all the stories Jesus told, they are parables: they teach us more about God. This is the story of how a sheep wandered off and got lost.

Ali Baa Baa

Slowly… close your eyes. Listen hard. Can you hear them bleating? Yes, it sounds like a whole flock of sheep. We are up on a hillside near the Sea of Galilee.

Below us, the land slopes down to the sea. Above us, the hill reaches almost into the clouds. Around us, there are sheep as far as we can see. Some are nibbling the grass by the rocks. Some are in the open. Some have climbed much higher up the hill. I don't understand how the shepherds can possibly know where they all are or how many there should be.

It's a very hard life, being a shepherd. You have to spend day and night out in the open with your sheep. What was that noise? Did you hear it? It sounded like a wolf howling. There are wolves in these hills and there's nothing they like better than sheep for lunch. Shepherds have to be very brave, because not only are there wolves but there are also bears. A bear will take a lamb from the flock if it is really hungry.

Look, the shepherd over there is trying to count his flock. It's not very easy because the sheep never keep still. But these shepherds know each one of their sheep. They even give them names.

Oh dear, he seems to be one short. Can you hear? The shepherd is calling out the name of the missing sheep. 'Ali! Ali!' The name echoes around the hills, but no sheep has come running. There must be a problem.

The shepherd is driving all the other sheep into a circle

made from rocks. They'll be safe in there. He's picked up a heavy wooden club and his long wooden crook. Do you see, there is a hook at the end of the crook? He uses it for pulling sheep out of any holes they might fall into.

Off goes the shepherd. We'll follow him from a distance. He's calling out the name of the sheep again and again. 'Ali! Ali!' It's quite a scramble over these rocks. Take care, don't fall down—the edges are razor sharp. I do hope Ali is going to be all right.

The shepherd is climbing higher and higher. He's searching behind every rock and down every hole. What a job! It's hard for us to keep up with him, but he is used to it. I hope there are no wild animals around—like hyenas or jackals. We're out of breath but he still manages to shout as he climbs. 'Ali! Ali!'

Quiet! Don't move. Listen. Was that a very faint baa? Yes, I think it was... and so does the shepherd. Now he is running towards that old prickly thorn bush. There's just a little woolly white bit showing. It has to be Ali.

Now we can really hear Ali baa-ing. His tail is wagging just like a dog's. The shepherd has taken out a knife and is cutting Ali free. He checks the sheep over to make sure it isn't hurt. I think it's more hungry than hurt. The shepherd lifts the sheep on to his shoulders and makes his way back to the rest of the flock.

I'm glad that's over... and so is Ali! All the shepherds have come together. They are having a party to celebrate Ali's return to the flock. Judging by the noise the sheep are making, they are having a party too. We had better leave them to get on with it.

Follow-up

How do you think the shepherd felt when he realized Ali was missing? How do you think Ali might have felt? How did the shepherd feel when he found Ali?

Prayer

Dear Lord Jesus, sometimes we wander off and our families worry about us until they find us. Help us to remember that we have to let people know where we are, and not to cause them any worry. Amen

Feelings 3

The man who helped

 Theme
Caring for others

 Bible verses
Luke 10:25–37

 Artefacts
Some ointment and bandages
Picture of a rocky road

Introduction

Show the children a picture of the Holy Land when Jesus was alive. Talk about the way people travelled then. What would the roads have been like? How would they differ from our roads today?

What does it mean to get mugged? Why do people mug other people?

Mugged!

Slowly… close your eyes. In our story we are going to travel a long way. We are going back to Judea at the time when Jesus lived there. Can you see the hills? They are quivering in the heat. It's very hot and very dusty. Just over there is the city of Jerusalem. In front of us, a road leads out of the city. There don't seem to be many people using the road.

Look! A man has just passed through the city gate. He's heading towards Jericho, 15 miles away, on his own. That's unusual. Most people travel in groups on this road. The reason is that single travellers often get mugged in the hills. I hope he's going to be all right.

The road winds round the hills. It won't be easy keeping an eye on him.

Look, he's stopped. Can you see why? That's right, he's having a drink. He keeps water in the goatskin bag slung over his shoulder.

Now our traveller has started walking again. You can follow the way he goes by the little cloud of dust. Do you think he feels lonely on that road? There's still nobody else about. Wait a moment. Did you see a movement behind those rocks?

Yes. Three men. They seem to be hiding. Our traveller hasn't seen them. He's still walking along the road towards them.

Did you see that? One of the men has jumped out in front

of the traveller. He seems to be talking to him. Oh no! The other two have crept out from behind the rocks. They're creeping up behind him. They have sticks in their hands. It's no good shouting—he won't hear us.

They've knocked him to the ground. Now what are they doing? They are stealing everything he has—his goatskin water bag, most of his clothes and his money. Surely they can't just leave him there? Yes, they can. The three muggers have run off into the hills.

Oh dear. Things don't look very good for our traveller. He's just lying there in the dust. The sun is beating down and he has no water. It all looks hopeless.

Wait a moment. Can you see? There's someone coming up the road. It's a priest on his way to Jerusalem. He'll stop and help…

I don't believe it. The priest had one look and crossed over to the other side of the road.

Another hour has passed. The traveller has hardly moved. Do you think he's given up any hope of help? Would you?

There's a small dust cloud down the road. It must be someone else. Perhaps the muggers are returning. No, it's another traveller. He'll stop and help…

I don't believe it. He's had one look and crossed over to the other side of the road.

That's it. There seems to be no hope at all. Our traveller is just lying there. He seems to be asleep. I think he's given up.

But wait a moment. Can you see? Coming round a bend in the road is a man on a donkey. Do you think he will go right by like the others? No. He's stopped. He's got off the donkey. He looks at the traveller. Now he's sat him up and is giving him a drink. He's seen the cuts and bruises left by the muggers. Now he's putting on ointment and bandages.

The sun is beginning to sink. It's harder to see what's happening, but our traveller is now on the stranger's donkey. What a hero! How do you think our traveller feels now?

Follow-up

Can you act out a little play with your friends that tells the story of the traveller? Who will be the traveller, and the muggers? (Remember not to hit the traveller, just pretend!) Who will be the people on the road?

What things will you say in your play? How will you show what is happening? How will you show the feelings of the people in the story? You may like to show the rest of the class at the end.

Prayer

Dear Lord Jesus, help us to recognize when people need us, and help us to know what to do. Don't let us be like the people who passed the traveller by. Instead, let us be like the man who stopped to help. Amen

Feelings 4

The story of Zacchaeus

 **Theme**
Experiencing a change of heart

Bible verses
Luke 19:1–10

Artefact
A bag of coins

Introduction

Just imagine for a moment that you have enough money to buy a favourite CD. You go into a shop or supermarket, choose the CD and hand it over to the shop assistant. She takes your money, drops the CD in a bag, and hands it back to you with a receipt for what you have paid.

If you look at the receipt, you will see that a part of what you paid is VAT. VAT is Value Added Tax. It's this tax that goes to the government to help them run the country. Your tax pays for schools, the police, firemen, the roads and hundreds of other things. Taxes are the way the government raises money to pay for all these things.

Taxes have been around for a very long time. When Jesus lived in Galilee, there were lots of tax collectors who collected lots of taxes! For example, if you travelled along a main road you paid a tax, if you crossed over a bridge you paid a tax, and if you had a cart you paid a tax on each wheel.

Remember that the Romans were governing the country and they needed taxes to pay their soldiers. Men were appointed by the Romans to collect taxes. These men were very unpopular because they usually took more money than they should. Some of them became very rich. One of them was a man called Zacchaeus.

The little rich man

Slowly… close your eyes. Today we have travelled to the town of Jericho. Jericho is a very important town. Many travellers go through Jericho along the road to Jerusalem. The River Jordan flows by the town and lots of people cross the river at that point.

You can see how busy the roads are. There are camel trains setting off into the desert. There are donkeys pulling heavy carts carrying timber. Roman legions march through the town. There are strangely decorated tribesmen who have come into the town to buy food.

Look over there. Can you see the small boys climbing up the palm trees to harvest the dates? Perhaps they'll throw you some.

Jericho is just the place to be a tax collector. Do you see that rather short man coming out of his big house? That's Zacchaeus, one of the wealthiest men in Jericho. Yes, you guessed. Zacchaeus makes his money from collecting taxes.

If you believe the ordinary people, they'll tell you that he charges much more than he should. They hate Zacchaeus. Let's follow him and see where he's going.

Just ahead, a crowd seems to be gathering. Listen… can you hear what they are saying? 'Jesus is coming to Jericho.' 'He should be coming along this road quite soon.' They are waiting to see Jesus.

Look, Zacchaeus has disappeared. He's dodged round the crowd and run on along the road. Now what's he doing? Can you believe it? He's climbing that old sycamore tree! Not the thing you would expect from an important man like Zacchaeus. Perhaps he is worried that the crowd won't let him in. Perhaps he is afraid they might get their own back for stealing their taxes, and hurt him. Anyway, there he is, way up in the branches.

The crowds are right. It is Jesus. He's walking quite quickly along the road with some of his friends. The crowds are waving and cheering. I hope Zacchaeus doesn't fall out of the tree!

Whatever is happening now? Jesus has stopped right under the tree. Listen hard. Jesus has seen Zacchaeus and he's talking to him.

'Zacchaeus, hurry up and come down. I have to stay at your house today.'

I don't know about 'come down'. Zacchaeus has very nearly fallen down, he is so surprised. I don't think he can believe that Jesus has actually spoken to him. Off they go, with Zacchaeus leading the way.

Oh dear, can you hear what the crowd are saying? 'Zacchaeus is a greedy thief and Jesus has gone to eat with him!' It's taken them all by surprise.

We'll follow Jesus and his friends and try to find out what happens next. They must have finished their meal by now. It looks as though Jesus is just leaving. Hold on a moment, I think Zacchaeus has something to say.

'Jesus,' he says, 'I am giving half of my property to people who are less well off than I am. If I've stolen anything from anyone, I will give back to them four times more than I stole.'

I wonder what the crowd will think now. Having Jesus to stay has made all the difference to Zacchaeus. He knows he's done wrong and he's trying to put it right. He really must be a changed man.

Follow-up

What kind of a man do you think Zacchaeus was before he met Jesus? How do you think he changed after he met him? How do you think he felt before he met Jesus? How do you think he felt when Jesus stopped to talk to him? What might he do in future that was different from the old way he used to live?

Are there ways of being rich besides having money or possessions?

Prayer

Dear Lord Jesus, sometimes it's easy to be greedy and to take more than our fair share. We only think of ourselves and not of other people. Teach us how to think more of others and to be more like you. Amen

Fear on the lake

 Theme
Being afraid

 **Bible verses**
Mark 4:35–41

 Artefacts
A model of a small sailing boat
A picture of Lake Galilee

Introduction

Sit quietly and listen. Imagine that we are sitting by the side of a big lake. It is Lake Galilee. Listen… can you hear the water lapping the edge of the lake? The sun is quite low in the sky. It will soon be sinking below the range of hills that rise up behind us.

Look carefully. There's a group of men walking towards the lake. Can you recognize anyone? That's right, it's Jesus with some of his friends. I think they are going to get into one of the boats. Perhaps the boat belongs to Peter.

Jesus is looking tired. He's been really busy all day, teaching a huge crowd about God and his kingdom.

A storm at sea

Slowly… close your eyes. Two of Jesus' friends are rowing the boat carefully away from the shore. Now the sail is going up. The boat shows up against the darker shore on the other side. Now one or two more boats have joined the first.

Oh! What was that? Did you feel those drops of rain? It's getting darker. I hope we don't lose sight of the boats. Now the wind is blowing stronger. It often happens on this lake. One minute it's calm and the next a gale is blowing.

Can you see how the waves are getting higher and higher? The little boats are rolling from side to side—and up and down. The men are fighting against the wind as they try to lower the sails. The boats are bouncing around like toy boats in your bath. The waves are breaking over the sides of the boats and the boats are beginning to sink lower in the water. It's not looking too good for Jesus and his friends.

But it doesn't seem to be bothering Jesus. Can you see? He's fast asleep at the back of the boat. I don't know how he could sleep through this. But his friends are looking more and more frightened. I'm sure they are thinking of waking Jesus. Yes, one of them struggles to the back, trying to keep his balance as the boat rocks and rolls. He's shaking Jesus.

But what will Jesus do? The other men in the boat are watching anxiously as Jesus gets to his feet.

Jesus looks at the waves. I think he is speaking to the wind and the water. Suddenly everything has changed. The wind has died down. The waves are no more. The other men in the boat stand with open mouths. They cannot believe what has happened. All is quiet, and across the calm water we can just hear Jesus talking to his friends.

'Why were you afraid? Don't you have any faith?'

The storm has gone and so have the little boats. It's too dark to see them now. Tomorrow Jesus will be teaching on the other side of the lake. I think he must have gone back to sleep again in the boat.

Follow-up

How do you think the men in the boat felt when the wind and the waves were rough? How would you have felt? Do you think Jesus gave them a strange answer? What would you have expected him to say?

Prayer

Dear Lord Jesus, you lived on this earth to teach us many different things. Help us to learn to trust that you are with us when we get scared or upset. Amen

Feelings 6

Jesus wanders off

 Theme
Understanding that those who love us worry about us

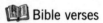 **Bible verses**
Luke 2:41–52

 Artefact
A picture of the temple in Jerusalem (see template on p. 147)

Introduction

'Don't worry, I'll be all right,' we say. But the people who love us and care for us do worry about us. They worry most when they don't know where we are and what we are doing.

Today's story is about two parents worrying about their son. The parents are Mary and Joseph and their son is…? That's right, their son is Jesus.

Jesus has just had his twelfth birthday. A Jewish boy becomes a man when he is twelve years old. In Jesus' day, as soon as he was twelve, every Jewish boy looked forward to visiting the city of Jerusalem for the feast of Passover. Passover is a very important festival in the Jewish religion.

Where can he be?

Slowly… close your eyes. Imagine that you are walking along a very dusty road. Sometimes the dust is stirred up when horses or donkeys trot past. Sometimes you are almost pushed off the road by a large cart or marching soldiers.

There are a lot of us in this group. We all set out from the little village of Nazareth two days ago. Look, over there are Mary, Joseph and Jesus. Jesus is looking very excited. You see, it's his first visit to Jerusalem and he's been looking forward to it for months.

'Are we nearly there?' That's what all the young boys are asking. It isn't far now. You can see the smoke coming from the fires in the city, climbing up into the clear blue sky. We shall soon see the buildings, especially the temple. That's where everyone is heading.

Every time another path or road joins our road, there are more people. There must be thousands, all making their way to Jerusalem for the Passover. No wonder Jesus is excited. You don't see crowds like this in Nazareth.

We must leave Jesus and his parents for the next few days while they celebrate the Passover and visit the temple. We will join them again as they begin the journey home. Mary and the other women start off first. They have a lot to talk about. Mary thinks that Jesus is with Joseph and the other men.

Joseph and some friends leave later—the men walk faster than the women. They plan to meet up again at the evening stop. Joseph thinks that Jesus has started the long walk home with his mother and some of the other young men.

Here we are at the camp where they will stop for the night. Mary is there with her friends. Look how surprised she is when Joseph arrives. Jesus is not with him.

'I thought he was with you!' says Mary. 'And I thought he was with you!' says Joseph. Can you see them searching the camp, asking everyone if they have seen Jesus? But no one has. Jesus is not there. There's only one thing for it—Mary and Joseph will have to make the journey back to Jerusalem.

The next morning, after a sleepless night, they leave their friends and head back up the road they walked along the day before. Joseph is walking so fast, it's really hard to keep up with him. Poor Mary is soon out of breath—and so are we. Do you see how worried they both are? I wonder where they will look in the city.

The search has begun. There'll be no sleep tonight. They go back first to where they stayed, but the innkeeper has not seen Jesus. He shakes his head. One boy among thousands —he could be anywhere.

Mary and Joseph search the markets. They look in the little shops down the narrow alleys of the city. They ask everyone they see, but no one remembers seeing Jesus. The city is much quieter now because all the visitors have started their journeys home. The people of Jerusalem are going about their daily work again without the crowds. At least it's easier to move in the city.

Can you think of anywhere they haven't looked for Jesus? Yes, there is one place—the temple itself.

Poor Mary and Joseph are exhausted. They have searched

everywhere—asked the question a thousand times. It looks as though they may give up. No, now they are hurrying through the streets to the temple. Someone, perhaps it was God, has given them the idea that Jesus might be in the temple. The sun shines off the white marble from which the temple is built.

We follow Mary and Joseph as they walk hurriedly into the outer courtyard. The temple is their last chance. They have looked everywhere else.

Do you see, just over there is a group of very clever-looking men. They are religious teachers who meet to discuss questions about God.

Suddenly Joseph gives a shout. 'There he is! It's Jesus.'

Joseph is right. Jesus is sitting in the middle of these teachers. He is listening hard to what they are saying and asking them questions.

Oh dear. Mary is looking like any mother does when she has been worried. She's very glad to have found Jesus, but angry that he went missing. I expect you know that look! I think that we should tiptoe away and leave Jesus to be reunited with Mary and Joseph. I'm sure they will make it home safely and together this time.

Follow-up

Have you ever been so absorbed in what you were doing that you forgot what time it was? Have you ever been late home because you were enjoying playing with your friends and didn't want to stop what you were doing? How did your parents feel when you didn't turn up when expected? Did you get into trouble? How do you think Mary and Joseph felt? What do you think Jesus said to them?

Prayer

Dear Father God, when we are excited about something, we don't always think of other people. If we get lost, we might not think about how our parents are feeling too. Help us to remember to do the right thing and tell our parents where we are. Amen

Feelings 7

The story of Martha and Mary

 Theme
Knowing when we're getting it right

 Bible verses
Luke 10:38–42

Artefact
Some pots and pans

Introduction

Think of a special friend. What is it that you like about him or her? Is it because you can trust each other? Is it because you like doing the same things? Is it just because you like being together?

There are lots of reasons why friends are important. One of them is that you can relax with friends and just enjoy being with them.

As soon as Jesus left home and started teaching and healing people, he became very busy. The crowds never left him alone. He had to get up very early in the morning to spend time talking with God his Father in prayer. As soon as people saw him, they expected him to tell them a story or make someone well. One place that he could go to relax and be away from the crowds was the home of his friends, Mary and Martha, in the little village of Bethany.

The two sisters

Slowly… close your eyes. We are in a house in the village of Bethany. The house does not look like yours or mine. It is single-storey and has a flat roof. Inside there is one large room. Off that are the kitchen and some smaller rooms.

There seems to be a lot going on. The two women in the house are very busy. They are sisters called Martha and Mary. It's definitely Martha who is giving the orders. Listen to her.

'Come on, Mary, they'll be here soon. The room needs sweeping. The washing-up has to be done. The meat needs preparing. The bread isn't in the oven. Stop dreaming and *get on!*'

Oh dear, Mary is in trouble. But hold on a minute. Martha said something about visitors coming. Who do you think they might be? One guess. That's right, the sisters are expecting a visit from Jesus and some of his friends. Martha wants the house clean, the food perfectly cooked, and everything to be right for Jesus. She wants Mary to help her, but Mary may have other ideas. Let's wait and see what happens.

That sounds like people coming. Have a quick look. Yes, there's Jesus and four or five of his close friends. Jesus looks rather tired. Once again he has been so busy—the people haven't left him a moment's peace. 'Please heal my mother.' 'Please tell us more about your kingdom.' 'Please make my little girl better.' And Jesus doesn't say 'no' to those who ask.

Now, he just wants a quiet rest before he walks on into Jerusalem.

Mary has popped her face out of the doorway. She sees Jesus.

'Martha, Martha, Jesus is here!' she shouts back into the house. Martha comes running out, drying her hands on a towel. She shows Jesus into their home. He looks pleased to sit down. Martha fetches Jesus and his friends a drink. She beckons Mary to follow her back into the kitchen, but Mary is sitting on the floor next to Jesus.

Jesus and his friends talk about the day, the people they have met and, more especially, what will happen when they arrive in Jerusalem. Look at Mary. She is listening to every word Jesus says. Martha's come to the kitchen door again. She's trying to catch Mary's attention, but Mary won't turn her face away from Jesus. The sound of pots and pans being banged about in the kitchen does not seem important to Mary. What is important is just being with Jesus—listening and learning from him while she has the chance.

Oh dear, I think Martha's had enough of this. She's come storming into the room, red-faced and angry. Can you hear one of the pans boiling over? She strides across the room and stands by Jesus.

'Lord,' she is almost shouting, 'doesn't it bother you that my sister has left me to do all the work by myself? Tell her to come and help me!'

Now what will Jesus say? Surely Mary should be helping her sister prepare the meal for their guests?

Jesus looks up at Martha. There's a smile on his face. He holds out a hand towards her. 'Martha, Martha,' he says very calmly. 'You are worried and upset about so many things, but only one thing matters. Mary has chosen what is best, and it will not be taken away from her.'

We must leave that house in Bethany with the friends sitting down to one of Martha's great meals. I'm sure Mary helped to clear it up afterwards!

Follow-up

How do you think Martha is feeling in this story? How do you think Mary is feeling? Do you think Mary is being fair? What would be happening in your house if visitors were coming to stay? How do you feel about that?

Prayer

Dear Lord Jesus, we often lead such busy lives that we don't have time to sit and listen to the good things that you are telling us. We tend to be like Martha, rushing round and doing lots of things. Help us to be more like Mary, who was content to sit and listen to you because she knew how important that was. Amen

Feelings 8

John the Baptist prepares the way for Jesus

 Theme
Learning to appreciate what we have and to share

 Bible verses
Luke 3:2–18

 Artefacts
A jug of water or scallop shell, and a shallow bowl
Some dusters and a bottle of furniture polish

Introduction

Imagine for a moment that someone is coming to stay at your house. It might be a grandparent or an aunt and uncle. It might be an old friend of the family. One morning at breakfast, three or four days before they come, Mum tells you that they will be sleeping in your bedroom. You will have to sleep with your brother or sister.

You know what this means. Everything will have to be got ready. All those things you have tucked under the bed—the football shirt, the magazines, the funky shoes, the CD you lost weeks ago—they all have to be put away.

The poster that has been falling off the back of your door for weeks will have to come down. The clothes that never seem to find their way into the right drawer will need sorting. And when you have done all that, Mum comes in with a duster, furniture polish and the vacuum cleaner. Your bedroom will be hardly recognizable.

Getting ready for God

Slowly... close your eyes. We are going back to Bible times—this time to the desert near the River Jordan. Just ahead of us, there's quite a crowd. There are some soldiers, some tax collectors and lots of ordinary men and woman.

Standing on a rock, with the wind blowing through his long tangled hair, is a very strange-looking man. His name is John. He seems to be wearing clothes made from camel hair. Can you hear what he is shouting?

'Turn back to God and be baptized. Then your sins will be forgiven.'

The crowd are listening hard to what he is saying, even though he is not being very polite about it. He has just called them snakes!

'Do something to show that you have really given up your sins.'

The crowd look puzzled.

'What should we do?' some of them ask.

'If you have two coats, give one to someone who hasn't got any. If you have food, share it with someone else.' John knows that there are many people who have more than they need, and many who do not have enough. Do you think this crowd will do what he says?

Now it is the turn of the tax collectors to ask a question. You remember how unpopular they are. They take more money than they should and keep it for themselves. What is John going to say to them?

'Don't make people pay more than they owe.' In other words, be fair and be honest. Be good tax collectors, not selfish ones.

Some soldiers have gone over to him.

'And what about us? What do we have to do?'

John looks them straight in the face. He may live in the desert but he knows what goes on in other places. He knows how sometimes the soldiers bully people to get money to make them go away.

'Don't force people to pay money to make you leave them alone. Be satisfied with your pay.'

More questions now—John has got the people thinking. Could it be that he is the Messiah? That's the question. Could John be the one sent from God to lead the people into a new kingdom? John shakes his head at this idea.

'I am just baptizing with water. But someone more powerful than me is going to come. I am not good enough to take off his sandals and wash his feet.'

Who is John talking about? That's right, it is Jesus. John has come to prepare the way for Jesus. John knows that he is doing God's work, but that Jesus is far greater than he will ever be. John says he isn't even good enough to be the slave that washes people's feet when they arrive at a house.

John climbs down from the rock. Look, he is heading for the river. Some of the people are following him into the water. He dips them under the surface of the water as a sign that they will change their ways. They look so much happier as they come up out of the water.

Over there, walking along the river bank, is a man we have not seen here before. He is going up to John. Do you know who it is? That's right, it's Jesus. I do believe that Jesus is asking John to baptize him. What will John say?

'Jesus, I ought to be baptized by you. Why have you come to me?'

After all, Jesus is the one whom John has been speaking about. He really is the Messiah. It is Jesus for whom John has been preparing the way.

'For now, this is how it should be, because we must do all that God wants us to do,' says Jesus. And John leads him down into the water for baptism. Jesus, the Son of God, was humble enough to be baptized.

As Jesus comes up out of the water, we must leave him with John. Soon after this, Jesus will start the work God wants him to do.

Follow-up

How do you think the crowd were feeling when John said some of those things to them? Do you think he said the things they were expecting him to say? What was he doing? Why do you think he was telling the crowd to share their things?

How do you feel about sharing your things with other people? How would you prepare for the arrival of a special guest?

Prayer

Dear Father God, we live in a world where some people have so much and other people have so little, they don't even have enough to eat. Help us to find ways to help people poorer than us, so that their lives may get better by what we do. Help us to appreciate what we have and to learn how to share good things with others. Amen

Feelings 9

Peter is rescued

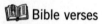 **Theme**
Knowing that God listens when we pray

 Bible verses
Acts 12:1–17

Artefact
A link of a chain or a piece of rope

Introduction

One of the best-known of the leaders of the early church was
Peter—the same Peter who had been a fisherman, and the same
Peter who, when Jesus was arrested, said he did not know him.
Now, after the Holy Spirit had come at Pentecost, Peter was a very
brave leader.

At the same time, King Herod began to cause a lot of trouble for
some members of the church. He had some of them arrested and
thrown in jail. When he saw that this pleased the religious leaders,
he had Peter arrested as well.

Peter was thrown into jail during the festival of Unleavened
Bread. At the end of the festival, the king intended to put Peter on
trial. But the church never stopped praying to God for Peter.

Behind bars

Slowly… close your eyes. We are returning to Jerusalem in the years following Jesus' death and resurrection. But this time we are not in the busy streets or even a private house. This time we have gone to jail!

It is very dark in here and it doesn't smell very clean either. In a minute or two, your eyes will become used to the light. That's better, now we can see more clearly.

Look, just over there are four Roman soldiers. Can you see their swords? Two of them are guarding the door. The other two are chained to a man—one on either side of him. The man's right hand is linked to the soldier's left hand and his left hand to the other soldier's right hand. In other words, he cannot move without disturbing the soldiers.

Listen! A senior soldier—he may be a centurion—has come over to the prisoner and is standing in front of him.

'You, Peter from Galilee, will be brought to trial when the festival is over. By the way, I don't think much of your chances!'

The other soldiers are laughing. They know what will happen.

So, this is not any ordinary prisoner. It is Peter the church leader. Every three hours, the guard changes. That means there must be lots of soldiers to make sure Peter does not escape. Some chance with all those chains round him!

Time is running out for Peter. Tomorrow the festival ends

and the king will put Peter on trial. Can you think what his friends might be doing at this time? Yes, you're right. They are praying that God will help Peter.

Was that you yawning? I must say I feel tired. Peter is certainly asleep. He's a brave man to sleep before he goes to court.

What was that? Keep it quiet, we do not want to wake the soldiers. There is a light flashing around the prison. It's not just a light… it's an angel. Look, he has gone over to Peter and poked him in the side. Peter has woken up.

'Quick! Get up.'

Look, can you believe it? The chains that bound Peter to the soldiers have fallen off and are lying on the ground. It has all happened so quietly that the soldiers haven't stirred.

'Get dressed and put on your sandals and your coat,' says the angel. 'Now follow me.'

I'm sure Peter thinks he is dreaming. But it is all really happening. Keep as quiet as you can and we'll follow them. Do you see, they have tiptoed past more soldiers. But what about that big iron gate that leads out into the city? Surely the angel does not have the key for that. Well, well, he doesn't need it. The gate has just swung open of its own accord.

Now Peter is in the street. But where is the angel? He has disappeared as quickly and quietly as he came. Peter must be careful. It is still the middle of the night. There could be a patrol of soldiers about.

Peter seems to know where he is going. Down this street, round the corner, and he has stopped outside a house. Now Peter is knocking on the gate. I think this must be Mary's house—the Mary who is John Mark's mother. We know it is a place where Jesus' friends have been meeting.

Someone has come to the gate but she has run off again. She is so excited, she has gone to tell the others. But will they believe her? Can you hear what's happening?

'I tell you, it is Peter! It really is!'

'Rhoda, I know we have been praying for Peter, but he can't have got out of prison.'

'*But it is Peter!*' shouts Rhoda.

'You're mad,' says someone. 'Perhaps they have already killed him and it's his angel.'

'Well, I don't think angels would bother to knock,' says Rhoda.

Some of the others have gone to the gate. They are amazed. Well, wouldn't you be? It is Peter standing there. Now they know their prayers have been answered. Peter quietens them down and gives them a message for James, one of the other leaders. Then he slips out of the house in the dark and goes away from the city to live another day.

And we must do the same.

Follow-up

How do you think Peter would have been feeling when he was locked up in jail? Do you think he was scared? How do you think he felt when he saw the angel? Do you think he could believe what was happening?

What do you think happened at Mary's house after Peter left?

How do you think Peter's friends felt when they realized that God had answered their prayers to take care of Peter?

Prayer

Dear Father God, you looked after the people who believed in you. They learnt that you were always there to protect them. Help us to learn how to trust you to look after us in our lives. Give us the confidence to know that you listen when we pray. Amen

Feelings 10

Paul is taken to Rome

 **Theme**
Knowing what it means to trust God

📖 **Bible verses**
Acts 27:1–44

◎ **Artefacts**
Holiday brochures showing Malta, Cyprus and Crete
Outline map for each child, showing the main ports, Cyprus,
Malta and Italy (see template on p. 148)

Introduction

(Show the map.) Malta is a small island in the Mediterranean Sea.
Many people nowadays go to Malta on holiday. One of the places
where they stay is called St Paul's Bay. Just off the coast is another
tiny island called St Paul's Island. Today's story happened on
Malta's coast nearly two thousand years ago.

Paul was travelling from Caesarea on his way to Rome. Soldiers
were taking him to be tried in Rome by the Roman emperor. (The
children can link the stops along the way with a pencil. The stops
are marked in bold type in the text.)

Captain Julius, from the Roman emperor's special troops, was
put in charge of Paul and some other prisoners. They boarded the

ship in the harbour at **Caesarea** and sailed along the coast to **Sidon**. Captain Julius was very kind to Paul and let him visit some friends in Sidon.

They left Sidon and sailed round the east coast of **Cyprus** (somewhere else that people visit today on holiday). They changed ship at **Myra** and sailed on to **Lasea** on Crete.

All the time, the weather had been against them. The strong winds delayed their journey. By the time they arrived on Crete, the sailing season had passed. It was too dangerous to sail in that area after mid-September. In fact, all sailing was stopped between mid-November and the middle of March.

Paul spoke to the crew and told them that if they sailed on, the ship would be badly damaged and some of those on board would die. Captain Julius took no notice of Paul and listened to the captain of the ship instead. They sailed again, this time hoping to reach another safer harbour where they could spend the winter.

On the rocks

Slowly… close your eyes. It is time for us to join Paul, Captain Julius and all the others on board ship. If you look to starboard (that is, the right-hand side of the ship), you can see the coast of Crete. Above us, the sails are flapping in the gentle wind. Just over there, on the deck, are Paul and Captain Julius.

I don't like to mention it, but it feels as though the wind is getting stronger. Can you feel it on your face? Yes, there are white caps on the waves and the ship is struggling against the wind. I hope you don't get seasick!

'It's blowing from the north-east!' That's the captain shouting. 'Lower the sail.'

The crew are fighting the huge single flapping sail—not an easy job in these gale-force winds.

The captain has come over to Captain Julius. 'We have no choice. We will just have to let the wind take us,' he shouts. I am beginning to wish we had stayed in Caesarea!

The weather is so bad, no one seems to know where we are. The ship is lower in the water than before. The captain has given an order to throw some of the cargo overboard to lighten the ship. I hope it works. Some of the crew are down in the hold, lifting the heavy sacks of wheat. Others are throwing the sacks into the sea. Careful! One of the crew nearly fell into the sea as a huge wave hit the ship. Hold on tight.

We can't see the sun in the day or the stars at night. The wind never stops howling. Everything is soaked through. Now the crew are throwing some of the ship's gear overboard —spare sails, ropes and wooden spars. Everybody is looking terrified.

'There's no chance now!' shouts a crew member as he struggles past us. 'We'll all be drowned!'

Listen, if you can, above the storm. Paul is speaking. 'You should have listened to me in Crete. If you had, this would not have happened. But I promise you, you will be safe. I belong to God. He will save all our lives. Only the ship will be lost. We shall be wrecked on an island.'

The sailors seem to think that we are near land. They are measuring the depth of the water. It's definitely getting shallower. Now they are talking about rocks!

What are those sailors doing? Some of them are trying to lower the lifeboat into the sea. I think they are escaping and leaving us to sink! Paul is speaking to Captain Julius again.

'If the sailors don't stay on the ship, there will be no chance of saving our lives.' That's done it—two of the soldiers have cut the rope and the lifeboat has dropped into the sea.

At last, it is light enough to see where we are. Thank God—just ahead is a small island. The sailors have raised a sail and are trying to let the wind carry us on to the beach. Suddenly the ship shudders and stops. Everybody is thrown around. The mast falls into the sea. The ship has struck a sand bank.

'Jump for it,' yells Captain Julius. 'If you can't swim, grab a piece of wood.'

Captain Julius has just counted all the prisoners, soldiers and crew. Not one has been lost. Everyone is safe, thanks to Paul—and God! We have come ashore on what will be called St Paul's Island, just off the coast of Malta. And that is where we must leave Paul—warming himself around a fire built by the friendly Maltese people.

Follow-up

How do you think the sailors felt when the storm blew up? How do you think the captain felt when Paul told him they would all be safe? How do you think the sailors and the captain felt towards Paul when they were all safe on the island?

Prayer

Dear Father God, long ago you looked after Paul because he believed in you. Look after us in our lives today and help us to want to learn all about the wonderful people who followed you. Amen

Appendix 1

Templates

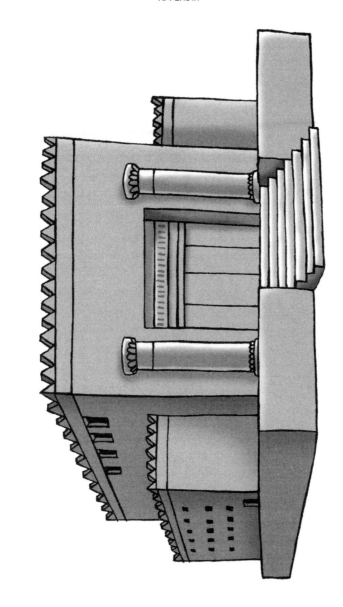

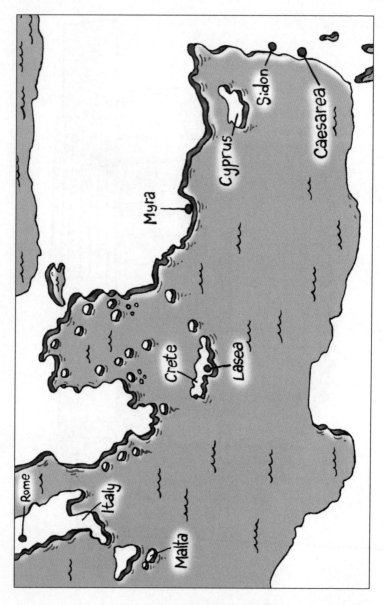

Appendix 2

Music suggestions to accompany the stories

- J.S. Bach, *Cello Suite No 1*, Prelude (02:55)
- Boccerini, 'Minuet' (*String Quartet in E major*) (02:14)
- Tarrega, *Recuerdos de la Alhambra* (03:55)
- Stanford, *The Bluebird* (03:41)
- Chopin, *Nocturne in E flat major*, Opus 9 No 2 (04:24)
- Morricone, *The Mission—Gabriel's Oboe* (02:20)
- Vivaldi, *Lute Concerto in D major*, second movement (03:48)
- Satie, *Gymnopédie No 1* (03:06)
- Elgar, *Chanson de Matin* (02:56)
- Dvorák, *Serenade for Strings* (04:41)
- Bizet, 'Act II Entr'acte', *Carmen* (02:12)
- Einaudi, *Nefeli* (04:11)
- Beethoven, 'Für Elise', *Bagatelle No 25* (03:11)
- J.S, Bach, *Piano Concerto in F minor*, second movement, BWV 1056 (03:23)
- Debussy, 'The girl with the flaxen hair', *Preludes* Book 1 No 8 (02:30)
- Schumann, 'Träumerei', *Kinderszenen* No 7 (02:33)
- Saint-Saëns, 'Aquarium', *Carnival of the Animals* (02:41)
- Offenbach, 'Barcarolle', *The Tales of Hoffmann* (03:18)
- MacDowell, *To a Wild Rose* (02:15)
- J.S. Bach, 'Air on a G String', *Suite No 3* (03:58)
- Grieg, 'Sarabande' *Holberg Suite* (04:08)
- Elgar, *Salut d'amour* (03:24)
- Barry, 'John Dunbar theme', *Dances with Wolves* (02:30)
- Fauré, 'Berceuse', *Dolly Suite* (03:15)
- Kreisler, *Liebeslied* (03:20)

Appendix 3

Index of Bible passages

Stories from Matthew's Gospel

Stories from Mark's Gospel

Stories from Luke's Gospel

Stories from John's Gospel

Stories from the Acts of the Apostles

★ ★ Also by Brian Ogden and Jo Dobbs ★ ★

News and Tell!

Twenty off-the-peg Bible themes for assemblies and the classroom

News and Tell! aims to provide busy teachers with an ideal off-the-peg package of biblical material for use at Key Stage One.

In this book, popular storyteller Brian Ogden joins forces with class teacher Jo Dobbs to combine delightful Bible-based stories with practical material for use in collective worship and *News and Tell* time in the classroom. Includes:

- Twenty Bible-based stories covering four key topics (Living Things, Food, Senses and Homes).
- Twenty *News and Tell!* activity pages with full photocopy permission, which can be built up as a personal RE topic work folder for each child.
- Extension work with additional ideas for each unit, for use in collective worship and the classroom.

The material can be used in conjunction with the QCA scheme of work requirements in RE for Key Stage One and PSHE/Citizenship within the National Curriculum.

ISBN 1 84101 198 3   £9.99
To order, please turn to the form on page 159.

★ ★ Also by Brian Ogden and Jo Dobbs ★ ★

Year-Round Assemblies

Thirty theme-based Bible stories for collective worship with follow-up activities

Year-Round Assemblies is a unique story-based resource book, designed to span three terms with ten collective assemblies in each, chronologically covering the lives of David, Jesus and Peter.

To provide a sense of anticipation and a break from traditional methods, without too much added work for already busy teachers, a variety of storytelling approaches are used. Some are told by an adult leader and include ideas for interactive storytelling; some are designed for presentation by an individual class or group and are child-led. Some are based on drama outlines, with two or three voices sharing the narration, plus inclusive participation using OHP or similar visual aids.

Each assembly plan includes suggested hymns from *Come and Praise* books 1 and 2. There are also three songs with simple on-the-page piano music, reflecting the lives of the characters featured, which have been especially written to accompany the material.

The extension activities cover a wide variety of PSHE/Citizenship objectives from the National Curriculum for Key Stages 1 and 2. Within the activities are elements for discussion, writing, drama and research.

ISBN 1 84101 328 5   £15.99
To order, please turn to the form on page 159.

Nursery Rhyme Nativities

Three easy-to-perform plays for pre-school and early years learning

One of the biggest problems faced by those working with very young children at Christmas is how to involve pre-readers in the nativity story with the minumum of fuss and manageable preparation.

Here is an ideal solution that will delight teachers and parents alike. In this book, popular author Brian Ogden offers three very diverse plays—all of which can be performed with groups of any size. Each one tells the story of the first Christmas from a different perspective, using well-known nursery rhyme tunes to bring the storyline to life. Simple directions, costumes and props ensure that the children are given the opportunity to participate fully in the performance.

ISBN 1 84101 236 X   £7.99
To order, please turn to the form on page 159.

Sing a Song of Seasons

Five easy-to-perform plays for pre-school and early years learning

There are many occasions during the course of the year when teachers working with very young children would like to involve their pupils in a simple dramatized presentation with manageable preparation and the minimum of fuss.

In this book, Brian Ogden offers five separate simple plays—all of which can be performed with groups of Foundation/Reception and Key Stage One children.

Simple directions, costumes and props ensure that the children are given the opportunity to participate fully in the performance, while songs written to popular tunes provide a helpful aid to involve the whole audience in the presentation.

The plays include three well-known parables—the prodigal son, the two builders and the farmer—as well as the story of creation and a very simple presentation of the events of Holy Week and Easter, written especially with very young children in mind.

ISBN 1 84101 364 1   £9.99
To order, please turn to the form on page 159.

barnabas

Resourcing **Storytelling, Drama, RE, PSHE/Citizenship, Circle Time, Collective Worship** and **Assembly**
in primary schools

- Barnabas Live creative arts days
- INSET
- Books and resources
- www.barnabasinschools.org.uk

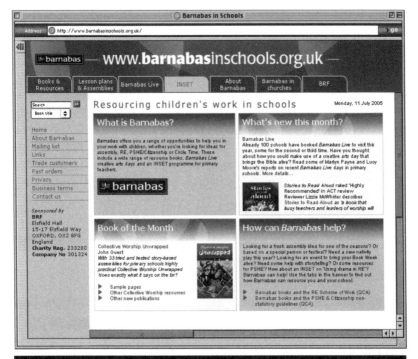